PHILIP MORRIS SCIENCE SYMPOSIUM 1973

the first
PHILIP MORRIS
SCIENCE SYMPOSIUM
RICHMOND, VIRGINIA
APRIL 26, 1973

PROCEEDINGS

Edited by NICHOLAS J. FINA

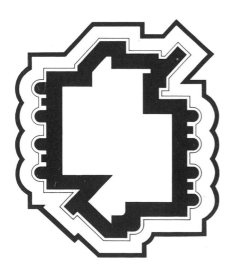

COVER DESIGN: a floor plan of the Philip Morris
Research Center .Tower, by James E. Day.

CONTENTS

A WORD
ABOUT
THIS BOOK

The first Philip Morris Science Symposium was part of a day-long ceremony on April 26, 1973 to dedicate a new building at the Philip Morris Research Center in Richmond, Virginia. This book presents the text of the five lectures which comprised the symposium, along with remarks by the dedication keynote speaker, **Dr. Glenn T. Seaborg,** Professor of Chemistry and Associate Director of the Lawrence Berkeley Laboratory at the University of California, Berkeley. The symposium speakers were:

* **Lord Todd, F.R.S.,** Master of Christ's College and Professor of Organic Chemistry, Cambridge University.
* **Dr. Milton Kerker,** Dean of Arts and Sciences at Clarkson College of Technology.
* **Dr. Neal E. Miller,** Professor of Psychology and Head of Laboratory of Physiological Psychology at the Rockefeller University.
* **Dr. Edward Leete,** Professor of Chemistry at the University of Minnesota.
* **Dr. J. J. Kirkland,** E.I. du Pont de Nemours & Company.

Dr. Helmut R. R. Wakeham

We were delighted to be able to assemble such a group of outstanding scientists for the inauguration of our symposia. As you will see in reading their reviews, all six speakers have developed uncommonly penetrating insights into their fields. We who attended the symposium found the talks quite rewarding. To share the experience we decided to publish the proceedings.

Together, the first Philip Morris Science Symposium and the official opening of a large, modern research tower demonstrate a principle which Philip Morris has always held in high regard: namely, that *open communication of scientific results facilitates the implementation of new knowledge.* Just as the Research Center Tower Laboratory demonstrates our own commitment to research and development, the symposium indicates to the scientific community our desire to engage in fruitful dialogue. As Dr. Seaborg observed in his keynote address, "never in the history of man have science and technology been in a better position to improve the quality of life for all mankind." We at Philip Morris believe that research and development will shorten the path to a better world.

Richmond, Virginia   Dr. Helmut R. R. Wakeham,
November 1, 1973   *Vice-president,* Research and
                              Development, Philip Morris, Inc.

Science, Technology, and the Quality of Life

We have reached a point in history where science and technology can eliminate most of man's past nemeses. At the same time we face new problems, such as pollution, over-population, and diminished resources. If we are truly to achieve a "democratization of privilege," according to Nobel Laureate Seaborg, we must learn to think ecologically and to better anticipate the full impact of our innovations.

BY GLENN T. SEABORG

The Changing Face of Natural Product Chemistry

From the perspective of four decades as one of the world's foremost organic chemists, Lord Todd contends that natural product chemistry in this century has moved in directions largely determined by the advent of new experimental methods. Major problems remain in the quest for an understanding of the relation between structure and function of natural substances. Solving these problems will have an important impact on both pure and applied science.

By Lord Todd, F.R.S.

Radiation Pressure
on Aerosol Particles

Scientists as far back as the time of ancient
Greece have observed and speculated on the
motion of small particles. One manifestation
of these phenomena, the interaction of light
with aerosol particles, is of special interest these
days to physical chemists investigating how
pollutants affect the atmosphere. Dr. Kerker
describes the theory he and his associates have
developed recently to explain these effects.

By Milton Kerker

How Psychological Factors
Can Affect Visceral Functions

You probably grew up assuming that your body does some of the things it does automatically, without affording you any controls. Professor Miller challenges this assumption with the hypothesis that functions of the autonomic nervous system may be no more or less susceptible to reward-and-punishment learning than functions of the somatic nervous system. Clinical applications may be possible, though none has been established as yet.

By Neal E. Miller

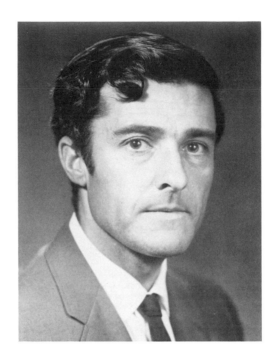

Biosynthesis and Metabolism of the Tobacco Alkaloids

What biochemical pathways lead to the formation and subsequent metabolism in tobacco of
nicotine-like compounds? Dr. Leete provides an
accurate and concise look at the current status
of this important problem. What we are learning today may someday lead to a better understanding of why the human body reacts as it
does to these alkaloids.

BY EDWARD LEETE

Experimental Optimization of Column Efficiency in High-performance Liquid Chromatography

If, as Lord Todd says (*vide supra*), the advance of natural product chemistry parallels the development of experimental techniques, the next several years should see some rather spectacular progress in organic analysis as a result of high-performance liquid chromatography. Dr. Kirkland, in the vanguard of researchers in this new field, speculates on the exciting possibilities.

BY J. J. KIRKLAND

Science

Technology

and

The Quality

of Life

Keynote Address by
GLENN T. SEABORG*

* Professor of Chemistry and Associate Director of the Lawrence
Berkeley Laboratory at the University of California, Berkeley

Never in the history of mankind have science and technology had a greater challenge to improve the quality of life. Never in the history of man have science and technology been in a better position to improve the quality of life for all mankind. Today I would like to speak about these challenges and also about the competing challenges made by the prophets of doom who berate science and technology as though they were animate and blame them for all our present-day problems. I shall advance the view that science and technology, if properly used, can combine to save our civilization and improve the quality of life for all of the world's people.

Recent Contributions of Science to Civilization

Applications of science and technology to the physical improvement of the quality of life are almost infinite in their number and variety. Illustrations in one of the fields of my own special interest come from the use of radioisotopes. One of the first dividends was in the production of food to help provide more efficient and economical fertilizing practices, better diets for farm animals, and increased milk, meat, and egg yields. Perhaps the greatest contribution has been in medicine, where some 30 radioisotopes are used in thousands of hospitals and clinics to diagnose and treat more than 4,000,000 people per year in the United States alone—a tremendous contribution to the alleviation of human suffering. And just earlier this month we learned of the implantation in a number of heart patients of cardiac pacemakers powered by a radioactive isotope. Radioisotopes are also making a substantial contribution to the world's industry, saving much money and benefitting the consumer with better quality and safer products.

Chemistry is providing most of the materials we live, work, and play with every day of our lives, including our food, clothing, housing, and life-saving drugs—creating the colors we see, the textures we feel, and the tastes as well as the nutritional values of the foods we eat. Physics is providing the magic of electronics upon which our revolution in communications is based. Through the biological sciences we are gaining an understanding of the life processes and of the many biological forces at work in ourselves and our environment. They have extended our life span and reduced disease and suffering, thus allowing us to enjoy longer and healthier lives.

Actually, of course, the fruits of these and other sciences are typically translated into beneficial use with the help of engineers and physicians and, we hope, increasingly with the guidance of social scientists. This team will be needed to solve the important problems of the future, such as the provision of the large amounts of energy required to sustain civilization and the alleviation of the environmental problems produced during the sustenance of that civilization.

In addition to these more practical applications, science and technology are contributing to the amenities and charm of living and to the increased pleasure of our leisure time. Here the contributions include widespread availability of good music through excellent, inexpensive reproductions of and means of playing music; the means for the restoration, authentication, and preservation of art masterpieces and other historic treasures, leading to enjoyment of these by more people; a rich variety of photographic and voice-recording equipment for personal and family use on a broad scale; the means to travel quickly over long distances effectively available to a large cross-section of people and making it possible to travel all over the world to historical and cultural centers and vacation spots.

These represent only a small sampling of the total picture. But an enumeration of the specific contributions of science and technology to the improvement of the quality of life is not my theme today; rather, my aim is to speak more broadly.

Human Liberation and Future Shock

For the first time in human history—within our lifetimes here—technology has made possible on a massive scale what an economist has called "the democratization of privilege." Until this century, multitudes of people could not afford to think about "quality of life" beyond the humblest provisions of food and shelter. Today increasing numbers of that multitude enjoy freedom from enervating, back-breaking labor; the means to travel and explore the world's wonders; the leisure to enjoy nature's beauty and new dimensions of one's own creativity. It is technology—particularly in the field of mass communications—more than anything else that has catalyzed such awareness in a vast spectrum of the world's people, that has enabled them to have time to concentrate their attention on needs beyond those of their personal sustenance and survival and, indeed, even to consider their well-being as interdependent with that of others.

This democratization of privilege through technology has also led to our having to consider problems about which we never have had to worry before. These are new problems, to be sure, but not necessarily portents of doom. If we want to shape the future—and particularly through science and technology—we must get out of the traps created by the despair of today's cynics or the frustration generated by unrealistic expectations. If it seems we are being told from all sides today that man is a failure, this comes about ironically enough because we are being judged in terms of a whole new set of standards in a world where almost everything seems possible, thus making every want, every injustice, and every wrong seem unbearable.

Many of these problems stem from the rapid acceleration in the rate of the development and application of technology originating from scientific research—this is one of the most beneficent and at the same time one of the most disruptive forces in our scientific age. Today, as a result of scientific advances, several complete revolutions in technologies are likely to occur in a single lifetime.

Let me cite just a few examples to illustrate this rapidly increasing rate of change. It took almost 2,000 years to go from the first practical demonstration of the steam engine to its commercial application. It was only 20 years, however, from the first practical demonstration of the radio to the first commercial radio station. It was only 12 years between the laboratory demonstration of the kinescope picture tube to the first commercial television production. And it was less than three years after the announcement of lasers that lasers could be bought on the commercial market.

These accelerating changes are having a fundamental effect on many interrelated aspects of our economy, the needs of our educational system and the future of our society. One result is that ours is no longer primarily a manufacturing economy. The United States is the first nation in the history of the world in which less than half of the employed population is involved in the production of food, clothing, housing, and other tangible goods. Our economy is becoming more and more an economy concerned with services, research and development, education, and activities made possible by larger amounts of leisure time.

One of the most significant results of this transformation from the age of the Industrial Revolution to that of the Scientific Revolution is the growth in professional and technical employment and the need for a more highly educated population. To cite engineering as only one example, in 1890 there were 800 workers for each engineer, but by 1960 there were only 75 workers per engineer. It has been estimated that between 1940 and 1975 the percentage of professional and technical people in our labor force will have doubled.

The speed of these changes has brought on a sense of societal "jet lag," a weariness at the prospect of more "future shock" and recurring laments about what some want to call "dehumanizing technology." We might say that science and technology have provided both the means and the necessity for us to re-examine our lives at this point. The life sciences prolong human life and create an exploding population, but they have also served notice on the possibility of ecological disaster. The physical sciences have given us the power to create change faster than we are able to manage it wisely, but they have also given us insight into that change. And they have provided the instant global communications that can sound an alarm over the conditions of man around the world and reveal with great impact our responsibility to each other.

To some people, the obvious solutions to this technological-sociological disparity are simple. They would return to the "good old days," viewing them through a strange pair of glasses, one that filters out our human advances as they approach the present and highlights only the "glories of the past." This group seems to forget that the glories of the past existed only for a small percentage of the population. Such glories were built upon the labor of slaves and the grinding poverty of the masses.

Another sizeable group of people would call a moratorium on all technological advances while we catch up sociologically. This approach will not work either. More than 40 years have passed since I first heard this moratorium suggestion. During the "Great Depression," it was suggested, considered, and discussed *ad nauseam,* and it seems just as unrealistic and depressing now as it did then. The advocates of this idea seem to forget that, while we would be stagnating scientifically and technologically, the rest of the world would be moving forward in these areas. And we certainly cannot even consider suggesting to countries less developed than ours technologically that they stop seeking better living conditions.

The Need for Systems Thinking

In the light of history I see only one realistic solution. That solution is to use all the scientific and technological knowledge that we have at our command. We must use this knowledge to correct past errors, to reverse harmful trends, and to anticipate and fulfill future needs; and we must coordinate all this knowledge in order to avoid blunders in the future.

In suggesting that science and technology can contribute so much to the solution of our present-day problems, I decidedly do not want to give the impression that I believe that all the criticism of them today is invalid or undeserved. Obviously the greatest problems of the quality of life in the United States today are direct by-products of the scientific and technological advances that first improved the quality of our everyday lives. The most common of these problems are brought to our attention daily when we read the newspaper, turn on the television set, commute to work in our automobiles. We see the air pollution; we hear the noise pollution; we read about or suffer energy shortages; we find the disposal of unwanted or worn-out goods as great a problem as the acquisition of those goods. These problems developed in a piecemeal fashion within our market economy.

Until most recently in our scientific age, we did not have the benefit of ecological or systems thinking—nor with expanding physical frontiers did we have the need for them. Specialization seemed to gain the most productive results. Everything invented or developed was used to the limits of its profitability, with its negative impact absorbed or written off, if noticed at all. And so we moved into what Simon Ramo has called the "century of mismatch" with unplanned or ill-planned growth, and leading to our current era when new limits, new interfaces, and all sorts of discontinuities have suddenly seemed to hit us just as we thought we had the "good life."

But today we are maturing in our awareness of this situation, so that the progress which is the end product of our efforts must be redefined in terms of a broad systems approach. From this awareness, a new set of standards is emerging and new guidelines for the course of society are being written.

The need for the systems approach—the ecological approach —is an important factor in itself. If we look around us, we see that many of the problems of our age are problems at new interfaces or that occur because of a lack of integration between related forces, both mechanical and human. For example, we no longer have merely a highway system, a railway system, and an airways system: we find ourselves with a total transportation system in which each of these components must flow together, although in the past most of the planning of each system was done independently and without regard to the other parts of the total system. If one component ceases to function or becomes overloaded, the backup immediately affects or even cripples the others. If we look one step beyond this, we can see that if our energy system—or any portion of it—fails, our transportation system is imperiled, our communications are affected, our health is endangered by the failure of other services, and so on. Similar critical relationships exist between the chain of resources, production and waste—and at the man-and-machine interface—as the role of man continues to shift from production to services. Modern civilization has such a complicated and interrelated structure that maintaining its balance as well as the smooth functioning of its parts is now essential.

Another of these new standards is in recognizing fully both the organic nature of human civilization today and its inherent relationship with the natural environment that supports it. Science and technology—the major forces behind the growth and intensification of these relationships—must be used to gain the knowledge we need to fill the important gaps in our physical and social intelligence and to adjust our discontinuities and coordinate our mismatched relationships. Future development cannot come through the direct exploitation of nature or man. It must be the result of using the capital of growing knowledge, of rethinking our values and revising our priorities, of learning to do more with less by increasing efficiency, by the maximum recycling of resources, by being more imaginative and less restricted by tradition in design, by learning to manage the greater complexity that is involved in the systems thinking and action we must employ.

This may require our building new social institutions (and perhaps restructuring some of our existing ones) to direct science and technology wisely. We must find ways to coordinate to a far greater degree the knowledge and actions of our life and physical sciences, and our behavioral and social sciences as well. Only a total synthesis of the knowledge of these disciplines, together with the insight of the humanities, will provide the degree of wisdom that society requires for its survival and development.

The key to our future, therefore, lies in our willingness to accept, understand, and master an ever-increasing degree of complexity. It is this route that will allow us to lead a life in which we can live in harmony with our natural environment, control destructive growth, and yet continue our creative evolution.

The scientific-technological era has brought us to the time when we are being asked to consider a wider range of criteria than ever before. We desperately need an increasingly aware general population, for whom limiting consideration to questions of economic profitability will not be enough. Fortunately, we are not faced with a strictly either-or proposition. Economic growth and ecological balance need not be incompatible. There are areas where new growth and development are essential, and there are areas in which they should be leveled off or even cut back. There is also a new morality being introduced into the marketplace that will allow economic values to be assigned to environmental necessities so that through a combination of regulations and incentives, we can enjoy a type of human advancement that is bound neither to a rising GNP nor to a harsh, zero-growth policy. The key to this bridging approach, however, lies mainly in the wise development and application of science and technology.

The Stimulus of Industrial Competition

What of the role of private industry in all of this? To have the "capital of organized knowledge"—as Galbraith has defined science—is one thing; but to have the incentive, the resources, and the management to apply it successfully is what really makes the difference. And these are what American industry provides. The competitive spirit, combined with ways of translating it into organized action, is what has made this country so productive— particularly as American industry embraced science.

If we look back over the past few decades, we can also see how dramatically our economic growth has been affected by industry's adoption of research and development and by the growing number of scientists and engineers taken into employment by our major industrial corporations. Science has proved a tremendous boon to free enterprise. That research and development is a basic element of competitive growth in this country is emphasized in the thought-provoking book "The American Challenge" by the French writer Jean Jacques Servan-Schreiber. In one of the many examples he gives to show to his fellow Europeans that basis of American economic strength through innovation, he points out that, "The U.S. chemical industry . . . now considers it normal that half its business is based on products that didn't exist 10 years ago." He also emphasizes how our industry has shortened the time gap between the laboratory and the production line.

The interaction between science and industry is also responsible for another productive effect, one that might be viewed as a form of spin-off from broad scientific thinking. I have in mind the new level of rationality adopted by business and industry—the use of operations research, systems analysis, and the various applications of programmed and computerized methods of planning and conducting business. This aspect of the science-industry relationship may well have the greatest beneficial effect on our society—particularly as it spills over into such areas as urban development and the resolution of environmental problems. I believe that private enterprise is responding in great measure to the call for a new social conscience. American industries, individually and through organizations, are taking important steps toward resolving urban and social problems. They are cooperating in many efforts to reduce environmental problems.

To call today for a rededication of science and technology to the cause of man, and to encourage the increased interaction of science and industry toward that end, is possibly to belabor the obvious. The occasion for our being here is a dramatic illustration that industry—and the people who guide it—can thrive in such a posture. As we commemorate the twentieth anniversary of Philip Morris Research, dedicate a truly impressive Research Center Tower, and inaugurate the Philip Morris Science Symposia, I congratulate and commend you.

The Changing Face of Natural Product Chemistry

By Lord Todd, F.R.S.*

* Master of Christ's College and Professor
of Organic Chemistry, Cambridge University

Natural Product Chemistry: Origins

There have been two definitions of organic chemistry. The earliest of them was that given by Berzelius at the beginning of the last century when he rather arbitrarily divided chemistry into two sections—inorganic and organic. Inorganic chemistry he defined as the chemistry of the mineral or inanimate world and organic chemistry as the chemistry of living matter. Now, of course, there was no scientific basis for such a division and it really served only to emphasize that the substances found in living matter did not seem to follow the same rules of behavior as mineral substances and were, in general, so complex that many people at that time believed that their formation involved a vital force which was to be found only in living creatures. It is commonly said that the vital-force theory received its *coup de grâce* when Wöhler synthesized urea in 1826, but this is hardly true. The theory lingered on in one form or another for a very long time after that, although it is true that it did not seriously interfere with the development of organic chemistry. The reason for this was not, however, Wöhler's synthesis. It was the realization that a characteristic of the substances in living matter was that they all seemed to contain the element carbon and the discovery at about the same time that coal tar was a rich source of carbon compounds. Since it was clear that little progress was likely to be made with the complexities of natural products (which is the common way of describing substances found in living matter) until a lot more was known about the element carbon and its simpler compounds, the attention of the early organic chemists turned to the coal-tar products and, for a time at least, the natural substances moved rather into the background and questions about vital force ceased to be of any great moment. It was for this reason, too, that around the middle of the nineteenth century in Gmelin's famous textbook the second definition of organic chemistry appeared: the chemistry of the carbon compounds.

Now, of course, neither of these definitions is wholly satisfactory. There are some carbon compounds, consideration of which is usually excluded from organic chemistry; again, it is probably true to say that the majority of carbon compounds known today do not occur in living matter at all. And yet, I confess that the Berzelius definition still attracts me and I should not like to see it abandoned. Throughout its history the chemistry of natural products has provided not only the spur to many experimental advances in organic chemistry but to most theoretical progress as well. After all, the discovery of the purple dye *mauveine,* which really founded the organic dyestuff industry, was made by W. H. Perkin in an abortive effort to synthesize the natural drug quinine. Later, the anthraquinone and indigoid dyes stemmed respectively from the work of Graebe and Liebermann on madder and of Baeyer on indigo. Polymerization work and the plastics industry can be traced back directly to the work of Harries on natural rubber. On the theoretical side it was Pasteur's work on tartaric acid that paved the way to stereochemistry through the theories of van't Hoff and Le Bel. The important concepts of dynamic stereochemistry and of conformational analysis due to Hassel and Barton can be traced back to the theoretical work of Hückel on the fused ring system of the decalins. What is perhaps less well known is that Hückel received the stimulus to that work from the studies on natural sterols being carried out by his colleague Adolf Windaus. Again, to take an even more recent example, the ideas of conservation of orbital symmetry and the so-called Woodward-Hoffman rules derived in part at least from synthetic work aimed at vitamin B_{12}.

The original impetus to natural product chemistry—and, indeed, the move to divide chemistry into inorganic and organic sections—undoubtedly came from medicine and the use of natural drugs in its practice, and was partly scientific and partly commercial in character. Already in the eighteenth century what could be described as scientific medicine was getting under way and drugs such as extracts of *Cinchona* and *Digitalis* were being used rationally. Again in connection with medical work cholesterol was isolated and described by Poulletier in 1780. First the pharmacists and then the chemists—actuated by curiosity or by the prospect of financial reward—began to busy themselves with the extraction and purification of the active principles of natural drugs and to study their chemistry. But this turned out to be far from easy in early days of organic chemistry, and during the nineteenth century the study of natural products took second place to the study of carbon chemistry employing simpler materials; this was work which was necessary if the foundations were to be laid for natural product chemistry. This is not to say that natural products were wholly neglected during this long period. There were indeed a number of hardy souls who kept on at the rather thankless task of studying animal constituents and trying to understand their functions. These were the physiological chemists from whom in time there came the development of biochemistry. The unfortunate separation between biochemistry and organic chemistry which developed and which is only now showing welcome signs of disappearing, was undoubtedly a reflection of the dominance of "carbon chemistry" among the organic chemists of the late nineteenth century and the concurrent rise of the great organic chemical industries with their emphasis on synthetic chemistry.

One cannot, of course, put precise dates to changes in scientific patterns, but round about the beginning of the twentieth century natural product chemistry started once more to come to the forefront of organic chemistry. One reason for this, no doubt, was the appearance of some scientific giants in the field—Perkin, Willstätter and Fischer, to mention but three. But there was, in my view, more to it than that. Organic chemistry had by then progressed to a point where it had the experimental techniques and, just as important, the background of knowledge and theory necessary to permit real progress in the study of complex natural substances. Furthermore, the rise of the organic chemical industry and the growing outlets for new materials encouraged work on natural products aimed at producing synthetic analogues which might at once have their virtues and be free of their defects, just as synthetic dyes had in many cases proved more useful than their natural counterparts. Finally, the steady advance of scientific medicine and the opening up of tropical colonial territories by the major European powers provided a further stimulus to the search for new natural drugs and their synthetic analogues as well as to the study of body components both normal and pathological.

Be that as it may, the fact of development of natural product chemistry is not in doubt and it has increased in prominence steadily during the century. During the first quarter or so of the century the broad structural features of the terpenoids of essential oils were established by Perkin, Wallach, and others. Willstätter's studies on chlorophyll and the nature of enzymes were carried out, and Emil Fischer made his brilliant investigations on the proteins and carbohydrates and his preliminary foray into the complex realm of the nucleic acid components. Perkin and his brilliant pupils Thorpe, Simonsen, Haworth and especially Robinson greatly extended our knowledge of terpenes, natural coloring matters, alkaloids, and carbohydrates. The schools of Windaus and Wieland explored the sterols and bile acids, while Hans Fischer moved ahead with his monumental studies on the blood pigment and other porphyrin derivatives.

Not all of these studies in the early decades were crowned with success. To quote but two examples, Willstätter's work on enzymes ran into acute difficulties and Fischer was halted in his protein studies after a brilliant start. These failures, like many others, were due essentially to imperfections in experimental technique. In natural product chemistry the old German saying *"Jeder Fortschritt der Wissenschaft ist ein Fortschritt der Technik"* is particularly applicable.

The Importance of New Techniques

It is therefore appropriate to recall here how the tremendous advances we have seen in the past 30 to 40 years have been conditioned and made possible by development of ever more powerful and sophisticated experimental tools. The first major advance was the development of reliable micro-analytical methods by Pregl—a development whose tremendous importance is sometimes overlooked. To be able to cut the amount of a scarce natural material needed for analysis by a factor of about a hundred made possible the exploration of fields hitherto barred to the chemist. But micro-analysis was only the first of the big improvements. Later came the introduction of chromatography—first by adsorption on alumina as developed initially by Kuhn and Brockmann, then partition chromatography on paper, ion-exchange chromatography, gas chromatography, thin-layer chromatography, and in the last year or two the amazingly powerful technique of liquid chromatography under pressure. Alongside these have come countercurrent distribution, electrophoretic methods, and many others which in sum have made the separation and study of complex macromolecules like proteins, polysaccharides, and polynucleotides possible for the first time.

Just as great an impact has been made by the new physical methods of analysis which have one after another been added to the organic chemist's armory. First came the application of ultra-violet and then infrared spectroscopy, followed by the extraordinarily powerful techniques of nuclear magnetic resonance, electron spin resonance, mass spectrometry, and recently photoelectron spectroscopy. These and others coupled with the techniques of X-ray and diffraction analysis applied to crystalline materials have been of enormous service and have provided in some cases a complete or virtually complete solution of structural problems which would otherwise have been, practically speaking, beyond the chemist's reach. Finally, the availability of radioactive isotopes stemming from nuclear research has opened up wholly new vistas in the study of biosynthesis and biodegradation in living organisms.

Natural product chemistry, like science in general, has tended to advance irregularly on a broad front during this century and during each phase of its development there were always individual investigators who stood rather apart and who broke new ground or saw possibilities not apparent to others at the time. For this reason, it is difficult particularly with such recent events to put precise dates to changes in scientific patterns. But in broad terms it seems to me that during the first 25 to 30 years of this century organic chemists in the field were preoccupied almost exclusively

with the structure of compounds and hardly at all with their function. Biochemists who were beginning to develop in this period
were just the reverse: interested almost exclusively in function.
Even Robinson's biogenetic theories, which later were to have a
profound influence on structural studies and biosynthetic work,
were put forward to underline structural relationships of a formal
nature and had no biological basis. This preoccupation with structure led to the development of a vast array of experimental methods, not only for structural elucidation but also for the synthesis
of molecules, and our catalogue of types occurring in nature increased by leaps and bounds.

This process, of course, did not stop in the 1930's. New
methods still came forward and older ones were improved, so that
today the organic chemist's methods of synthesis are so powerful
and so sophisticated that the total syntheses of such monstrous
molecules as that of vitamin B_{12} and even of macromolecular
enzymes like ribonuclease have been achieved. But let us face
the fact that, in the past, many people have regarded the natural
products merely as suitable materials on which to exercise their
chemical ingenuity rather in the way that they might look at a
difficult crossword puzzle. This kind of approach has doubtless
greatly increased our store of factual knowledge, but I rather
doubt whether it will nowadays lead to any major advances in
science, however valuable it may be for industrial development.
Certainly its importance to progress in organic chemistry has, in
my view, been dwindling since about 1930.

Structure and Function in Natural Products

It was, in fact, just about 1930 that a new interest began to
appear, slowly at first and later with increasing rapidity: an interest
in structure in relation to function among natural products. It is
this which has brought organic chemistry much closer to biology
than ever before. Equally, the growing recognition that function
must be considered in relation to structure has brought biochemists
and organic chemists together to the considerable advantage of
both. What brought about this change? I believe it was the gradual
movement of biology, spurred on perhaps by biochemical work,
away from purely taxonomic and descriptive studies. A major

influence was exerted by work on accessory food factors or vitamins. The study of nutritional problems had reached by the late 1920's a point at which it was realized that with adequate biological test methods available the mysterious vitamins might in fact be isolated and submitted to chemical investigation. The opportunities were seized upon by the chemists as were the similar ones presented by, for example, the secondary sex hormones. Structures were worked out and soon synthetic vitamins, hormones, and their analogues became available. But it was inevitable that the organic chemists who entered this field in the 30's should become fascinated by the further questions arising from it: why and how do vitamins and hormones act and what is the secret of their specificity? And so the advancing front of the subject began to take a definite orientation toward the solution of biological problems. This reorientation of natural product research falls into two sections for, although it is obviously aimed at the solution of biological problems, biosynthesis really stands a little apart from the type of work above indicated; I shall have something to say about it a little later.

The new trend is well illustrated by my own career, since I was myself one of those who was involved in it. I and my colleagues in the mid and late 30's applied ourselves to the vitamin field, pursuing structure and synthesis of vitamins B_1 and E on the classical pattern. Just at this time, however, workers in the field of enzymology found that the coenzyme of the carboxylase of yeast (which decarboxylates pyruvic acid) was, in fact, the pyrophosphate ester of vitamin B_1 (thiamine pyrophosphate), that vitamin B_2 was part of a second coenzyme (flavin-adenine-dinucleotide) involved in redox processes in living organisms, and that nicotinamide was a structural element in cozymase. These findings clearly indicated why vitamins were so important, although required only in small amounts. But they also indicated that if one wished to understand their specificity in action it would be necessary to study the coenzymes—to confirm structures by synthesis and to study synthetic analogues in biological systems. Our work, then, moved along these lines and we did, in fact, synthesize a number of major coenzymes.

Synthesis in the coenzyme field, however, involved entry into the field of nucleosides and nucleotides and so, in due course, to the structure of nucleic acids—work which helped to trigger much of the modern development of genetics and molecular biology, as well as purely chemical studies in the polynucleotide field. This pattern could be paralleled in other areas and I single it out here merely as an example with which I happen to be familiar. In the early phases of this reorientation the chemist simply accepted from the biochemist or biologist substances such as vitamins or hormones whose existence had already been demonstrated. Over the years since then, co-operation through interdisciplinary research has increased, and often the chemist is involved at a very early stage in establishing whether a particular biological phenomenon has a chemical basis before he applies his refined methods to the actual isolation of the substance or substances involved.

Much has been done in this general area, but much still remains. The antibiotics provided an early example, but there are many others. Among them one thinks of work on the so-called pheromones, a rather loosely defined group of substances whose first discovered members were the sex attractants of insect species. We now know, of course, that pheromones are important in most animal species and possibly even in human beings. Closely related to the pheromones in a biological sense is what I believe to be a large group of substances which influence obligate parasitism both in plants and animals. These remarkable and extraordinarily active compounds are frequently so unstable and occur in such small amounts that their successful investigation has only recently become possible.

An example in the animal field is the so-called "potato-eelworm hatching factor" whose chemical individuality my colleagues and I established just over 30 years ago, and which we sought to study with the primitive techniques of the time (although we had, admittedly, only moderate success). The potato eelworm (*Heterodera rostochiensis*) is a tiny nematode worm which battens on the roots of the potato plant and causes immense economic damage in Europe. In its reproductive cycle it lies in the soil in the form of tiny leathery cysts, each containing several hundred embryo worms; these lie dormant in the soil without hatching until potatoes are planted in their vicinity. The growing potato roots secrete into the soil a substance (the hatching factor) which specifically causes worms to emerge from the cysts and (presumably by traveling up a concentration gradient) attack the growing roots.

An analogous substance from the vegetable kingdom is the specific factor which is secreted by host plants and triggers germination of seeds of parasitic *Striga* species in their neighborhood. Interestingly enough we also investigated this problem, but could only get a rather rough picture of the type of molecule involved. Just a month or two ago—nearly 25 years after our work on the *Striga lutea* factor—*strigol* was isolated and its complete structure determined by physical methods in the United States. The fact that this could be done adds to my belief that an enormous field is now ripe for attack in the study of chemical factors which ensure that a parasite will attack one species of organism and leave another closely related one untouched. Rather similar in many respects to these fast developing areas of pheromone and parasite factors is the expanding work on such physiological moderators as cyclic AMP, the prostaglandins, and so on. I foresee many years of continuing work in these fields.

Quite early this century—as soon, indeed, as the big surge in natural product chemistry got under way—some organic chemists became interested in the structural relationships which were evident in certain groups like natural phenolic substances and the alkaloids and various biogenetic theories were advanced. An early contributor was Collie, but perhaps the most significant contributor was Robinson, whose views on structural relationships among alkaloids had a lasting impact, and whose tropinone synthesis in aqueous solution at room temperature lent color to his views on alkaloidal synthesis in plants from simple amino-acids. It must be emphasized, however, that all these views were speculative and no experimental evidence in support of them was available. They were, in fact, biogenetic theories and did not necessarily bear any relation to what went on in biosynthesis. The reason for this is clear enough: one cannot study biosynthesis in a plant or animal without having some means of labeling starting materials, intermediates, and products. Efforts to do so were, of course, made but even the ingenious efforts of Raistrick to develop carbon "balance sheets" for mold growth proved fruitless. When the heavy isotope of nitrogen could be enriched in ammonia, Schönheimer in the late 30's was able to show that, given an isotopic marker, the study of biosynthesis would, in fact, be feasible. Whether the study of biosynthesis would have made much progress without the Second World War is, I suppose, open to question. One thing is sure: the work which led to the atomic bomb made readily available for the first time radioactive isotopes not only of carbon, but of many other elements, and this made it possible to make a real attack on the problems of biosynthesis.

As a result, we have seen striking advances in our knowledge of the intricate synthetic pathways in both higher plants and animals and in micro-organisms. I shall not attempt to enumerate these, but surely the elucidation of the biosynthetic pathways to the terpenoids and steroids due to the work of Bloch, Cornforth and Lynen makes one of the most exciting and beautiful stories in all science. In particular, the extraordinary stereochemical specificity of the methods used by nature and the apparently mild conditions under which the necessary reactions occur have, together with similar stereochemical specificity in vitamin-coenzyme-promoted reactions, been largely responsible for a new trend in natural product work which is even now beginning to come to the fore and which I believe will become increasingly prominent. This is not to say that work on the other two lines I have mentioned will cease, but I believe that work on enzymes could well become the major front in natural products during the next decade or so.

Toward an Understanding of the Chemistry of Life

There can be no doubt as to the central role of proteins in living organisms. True it is that the genes—the transmitters of hereditary characteristics—are nucleic acids. But the prime function of nucleic acids is to direct and control the synthesis of the proteins upon which the whole economy of the cell depends. Their functions are manifold. Although some have structural and other passive functions, the greatest importance attaches to the large number which operate in enzyme systems; they promote, mediate, and control almost every chemical reaction in the body, displaying in the process a quite extraordinary specificity and a power to bring about with apparent ease, in aqueous media, reactions which, in the laboratory, require the most drastic conditions if they are to proceed at all. Their existence has long been known; but although some of them were prepared years ago in a homogeneous condition, our knowledge of the enzyme proteins has until recently been very scanty—and indeed, it cannot be said that it is very advanced even today.

It is easy enough—and no doubt in a very general way correct—to envisage the protein part of a two-component enzyme as holding substrate and coenzyme in appropriate proximity to one another, so that reaction can proceed. In those cases (and they may well be in the majority) where there is no discrete coenzyme, the substrate is attached to the enzyme at the "active site" on the protein molecule which serves the same function as a coenzyme. This is, of course, only paraphrasing the old "lock-and-key" theory of biological action and it doesn't take us much further, although another facet, namely inhibition by competition with enzyme or coenzyme for substrate or *vice versa* has provided a rational basis for the design of therapeutic agents. It is true that to date the design of synthetic drugs on this basis has been less successful in a practical sense than the rationalization of activities already observed, but the reasons are fairly clear. In order to apply such an approach successfully, we need far more knowledge than we now have about enzyme action.

Nowadays we have methods by which we can determine the amino-acid sequence in protein molecules. This has enabled us in a number of cases to determine the precise difference in composition between enzyme proteins performing the same function in different organisms. Such differences are frequently very small, although apparently highly specific. From such sequence studies it has been possible to deduce—in some cases with a high degree of probability—the nature and location of the active site or sites. It has even been possible by X-ray-crystallographic analysis to effect complete structural analysis of certain enzymes. In one such instance, lysozyme, the active site appears to be located in a trough or hollow in the protein molecule which seems in shape and size very suitable for accommodation of a substrate molecule. But we must beware of jumping too readily to conclusions, for the physical (as distinct from the purely chemical) structure of a macromolecule is doubtless important in determining its reactivity, and it does not necessarily follow that the tertiary structure observed in a crystalline protein will be preserved intact in solution or suspension.

This question of size and shape of the protein molecule is vital in considering enzymes and their action. Many efforts have been made in the past to synthesize small molecules which, because of their similarity to or identity with active sites of coenzymes, would duplicate enzyme reactions under "physiological" conditions of room temperature and dilute solution. These efforts have been to no real avail. One of the secrets of enzyme action is, of course, that it does *not* take place in dilute solution. It is a function of the protein to take the molecules which are to undergo reaction out of the dilute macro-environment and bring them together in a micro-environment in which conditions are totally different. This it can do because of its size, its multiplicity of polar groups, and its relative acidity or basicity.

These are tremendous problems and I believe that the search for answers to them will be a major feature of natural product chemistry in the years immediately ahead. Success will not only be of value to pure science, but it will be important also to industry, for it will permit the large-scale use either of natural enzymes or of synthetic macromolecules which will act like enzymes with all that may mean in the lessening of pollution of our environment through manufacturing activities. It will be a fascinating field to work in, too, for it will compel the organic chemist to pay much more attention than he has done to the finer points of non-covalent bonding and secondary forces which operate at the macromolecular level.

I have tried in this lecture to trace the development of natural product chemistry through its various phases. At first sight it would seem to have undergone several quite distinct changes in pattern, but I wonder whether this is in fact so. In the earliest days of his science the organic chemist was attracted to the natural products not just for their structure but because he wanted to understand their function. He soon found that before he could deal with the latter, an enormous amount of work on structure was needed—work for which new techniques had to be found. From that time on one could reasonably argue that each change in emphasis and each acceleration of progress has rested on advances in technique and that these have exerted a decisive influence on the direction of natural product chemistry. I believe that this is indeed so. I believe that we now stand on the threshold of a whole range of new and fascinating researches on enzymes and biological moderators opened to us by the new physical tools developed in the past 20 years. Other techniques will succeed them and with them natural product chemistry will march on to new successes which will bring nearer a full understanding of the chemistry of life itself.

Radiation
Pressure
on
Aerosol
Particles

By MILTON KERKER*

* Dean of Arts and Sciences, Clarkson College of Technology

Hence there are as many types of motion or
change as there are meanings of the word 'is' . . .
namely . . . alteration, . . . increase and decrease,
. . . coming to be and passing away, . . . locomo-
tion. . . . Now . . . it is this latter, . . . motion in
respect of place, . . . that must be primary.

ARISTOTLE OF STAGYRA (384-322)
PHYSICA

It was the goal of Aristotle's adversary, Democritus, to reduce all phenomena to the locomotion of small particles called atoms. Movement was a primitive property of atoms which were further distinguished by shape and size. Other- wise, they were absolutely identical and the qualitative differences of things as perceived were only apparent manifestations of the deeper reality. The atoms were the ultimate grains of matter; they differed physically only in their size, their shape, and their move- ment. All other properties were banished.

'Tis thine to know the atoms need not color,
But render forth sensations, as of touch,
That vary with their varied forms. . . .
But think not haply that the primal bodies
Remain despoiled alone of color: so,
Are they from warmth dissevered and from cold
And from hot exhalations; and they move,
Both sterile of sound and dry of juice; and throw
Not any odor from their proper bodies.

TITUS LUCRETIUS CARUS (95-55)
OF THE NATURE OF THINGS

The atomic theory was among the philosophical concepts of the Greeks, which provided the setting for those developments in the seventeenth century culminating in modern physics, yet it is hardly necessary to belabor the point that our atoms are not merely small particles. Nor do the colloidal particles suspended in a gas which comprises aerosols nor those suspended in a liquid which comprises hydrosols and other sols conform to the Democritan atoms. Not only are they not indivisible, but they possess distinctive properties—density, thermal properties, electromagnetic properties, optical properties, etc.—which are the same as those in the bulk. They are not just undifferentiated matter in motion.

Colloidal particles are sufficiently large so that the laws of macroscopic physics suffice to describe them. Yet, because of their dimensions, they respond dramatically to the movements of gas molecules and to visible radiation and they behave phenomenologically in ways that cannot be interpreted solely by scaling down from bulk material to their dimensions. There are peculiar phenomena which depend strongly on the size and shape of the particles, and it is in this sense that they resemble the atoms of Democritus. For example, they undergo incessant Brownian motion, just as Democritus prescribed.

Brownian and Other Motions

Brownian motion is uniquely a property of colloidal particles. It took three-quarters of a century after Robert Brown's (1) description in 1828 of the movement of pollen grains suspended in liquids to establish the notion that this phenomenon has its origin in the random bombardment of the particles by the fluid molecules and that accordingly it is a direct manifestation of the reality of molecular movement. Yet Lucretius had already quite clearly delineated the model.

> *For thou wilt mark here many a speck, impelled*
> *By viewless blows, to change its little course,*
> *And beaten backwards to return again,*
> *Hither and thither in all directions round.*
> *Lo, all their shifting movement is of old,*
> *From the primeval atoms; for the same*
> *Primordial seeds of things first move of self,*

And then those bodies built on unions small
And nearest, as it were, unto the powers
Of the primeval atoms, are stirred up
By impulse of those atoms' unseen blows,
And these thereafter goad the next in size;
Thus motion ascends from the primevals on,
And stage by stage emerges to our sense,
Until those objects also move which we
Can mark in sunbeams, though it not appears
What blows do urge them.

How Richard Zsigmondy's (2) ecstatic description of his first ultramicroscopic observations upon gold sols might have delighted our poet!

A swarm of dancing gnats in a sunbeam will give
one an idea of the motion of the gold particles in
the hydrosol of gold. They hop, dance, jump, dash
together and fly away from each other, so that it is
difficult in the whirl to get one's bearings.

The particle undergoes a path of such extreme sinuosity under the incessant but random molecular bombardment that the detailed motion still defies measurement. Indeed, it was Norbert Wiener's (3) attempt to make precise mathematical sense of the ensemble of paths of a single particle that led him and others to develop much of the modern work in stochastic processes. Einstein's (4) approach was much more practical. He proposed instead that an observable quantity, the mean square displacement Δ^2 during an interval of time τ, be given by:

$$\Delta^2 = 2D\tau \qquad \text{(Eq. 1)}$$

where D is the diffusion coefficient. It was, at least in part, for experiments which attempted to verify this relation that Nobel prizes were awarded to Robert Millikan (1923, physics), Jean Perrin (1926, physics), and The Svedberg (1926, chemistry).

Aerosol particles may also undergo a variety of other types of motion which are superimposed upon the Brownian motion. A particle will fall under gravity until it attains a constant terminal velocity where its weight is balanced by its frictional drag. A charged aerosol particle will undergo electrophoresis in an electric field, and, if it has a magnetic moment, magnetophoresis in a magnetic field. Thermophoresis occurs whenever there is a temperature gradient in the gas. Aerosol particles move toward the region of lower temperature because the molecular impacts on the hot side convey more momentum on the average than those on the cold side. In a concentration gradient, aerosol particles will undergo diffusiophoresis as a result of a net force due to the diffusion flux.

The theory of these latter phenomena is still incomplete, particularly when the particle size is comparable to the mean free path of the gas molecules (5), and the complexities that one can encounter in nature are awesome. Consider the scavenging of atmospheric aerosol by a falling raindrop. Such scavenging cleanses the atmosphere and thereby enhances visibility and reduces air pollution, but it also results in radioactive fallout.

The problem, as depicted in Fig. 1, is to determine the fraction of aerosol particles of radius a in the path of the falling raindrop of radius A which is actually intercepted by and attached to the raindrop. The aerosol particles are held in the fluid streamlines by the viscous forces. If there were no other motions, the interception would be determined by the number of particles carried in those streamlines which pass within the distance a of the surface of the particle. However, because of their inertia particles will swerve out of the streamlines towards the raindrop and because of their Brownian motion they will diffuse in all directions out of the streamlines and some of these will be collected by the raindrop. On the other hand, if the atmosphere is not saturated, there will be evaporation with the attendant diffusiophoretic force, but this evaporation will be accompanied by cooling so that there also will be a thermophoretic force attracting the particles towards the raindrop. Finally, the presence of charges on the raindrop or the particles will set up electrophoretic forces. As if this were not enough, there will be eddies in the wake of the droplet, fluid circulation within the droplet, and flattening of the droplet, all of which complicate both the hydrodynamics and the collection. No wonder we are attacking this problem in our laboratory by direct

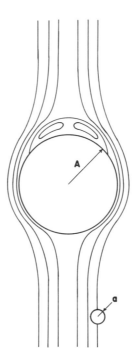

Fig. 1.   Aerosol particle of radius *a* in the streamlines
surrounding a falling water droplet of radius *A*.

measurements rather than by a theoretical analysis.

We cite the scavenging problem not only because of its importance in atmospheric physics, but also because elucidation of the motion of aerosol particles in this case is so similar to that in two other classical problems of aerosol physics—the capture of aerosol particles by a filter and the deposition of aerosol particles within the human lung system.

Still other motion of aerosol particles is caused by light, and that is the main subject of this essay. Two distinct motions can be ascribed to the action of light. Radiation pressure or light pressure has its origin in the scattering of light by the particle, but we shall see that it is also affected by the absorption of light. Photophoresis is due to the absorption of light and the consequent interaction of the gas molecules with the heated particle. We have recently (6) made a contribution to the theory of each of these effects which I will consider later.

Scattering and Absorption

The motion of the light itself is altered whenever it is incident upon a particle, and although that is not our specific subject it will be necessary to consider it first in order to understand more clearly how the particle is moved by light (7).

The geometry is shown in Fig. 2. The spherical particle with radius a is at the center of a Cartesian coordinate system with the electromagnetic wave incident along the positive z-axis. If the

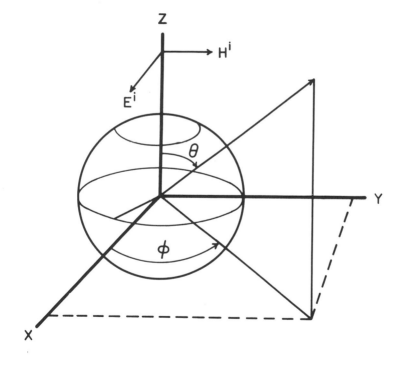

Fig. 2. Coordinate system for analysis of light scattering. The incident radiation proceeds along the positive z-axis. The direction of scattering is defined by the angle θ since scattering for unpolarized incident radiation will be independent of angle ϕ.

incident wave is unpolarized—*i.e.,* composed of two completely incoherent components of equal amplitudes whose electric vectors are mutually perpendicular—the scattered radiation is identical along any particular direction of the cone defined by angle θ, and the scattering is only a function of the scattering angle θ. The *y-z* plane will be defined as the scattering plane. The diagram in Fig. 3 sketches a view within this plane which will be useful even though it is a fiction. The ray *M* impinges upon the sphere and then divides into reflected and refracted rays upon each encounter with the surface. Its course within the sphere is depicted by i_1, i_2, and i_3 while r_1, r_2, and r_3 depict the external paths. The other ray *N* is not directly intercepted by the sphere, but it passes sufficiently close so that it will be diffracted as shown by d_1.

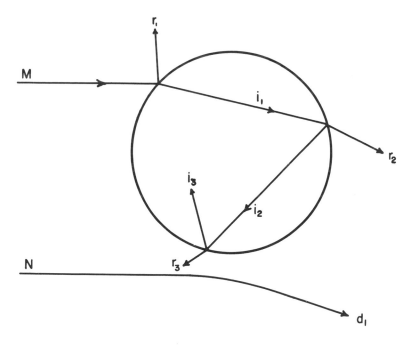

Fig. 3. A ray optics view of scattering. Ray M undergoes successive reflections and refractions (r_1, i_1, r_2, i_2, r_3, i_3). Ray N undergoes diffraction such as into ray d_1.

The external trajectories, both those resulting from reflection-refraction and from diffraction, comprise the scattered radiant energy. If the material of which the sphere is composed is absorptive, radiant energy will be attenuated as it follows along i_1, i_2, i_3, etc., because of its partial conversion into thermal energy.

The amount of radiant energy which is scattered per second is given by the scattering cross section, C_{sca}, the amount absorbed by the absorption cross section, C_{abs}, and the total by the extinction cross section, C_{ext}, so that:

$$C_{ext} = C_{sca} + C_{abs} \qquad \text{(Eq. 2)}$$

The cross sections are defined relative to the incident beam so that the power which is scattered or absorbed is precisely that contained in that part of the incident beam with cross-sectional areas, C_{sca} or C_{abs}, respectively.

The reason the representation in Fig. 3 is fictitious is because ray optics is completely inadequate to describe the propagation of light through or around small obstacles. Instead it is necessary to utilize the theory of electromagnetic waves based upon Maxwell's equations. The problem of scattering and absorption was solved in a quite general way for long circular cylinders at perpendicular incidence by Lord Rayleigh (8) and for spheres by a number of people at the turn of the century, including Ludwig Lorenz (9) and Gustav Mie (10).

Without going into detail we can outline the theory in a very general way with the aid of Fig. 4. There is a particle; there is an incident wave described by the electric and magnetic field vectors E^i and H^i; there is a scattered wave described by E^s and H^s; and there is an internal wave described by E^r and H^r. Electromagnetic theory requires that the tangential components of the field vectors be continuous across the boundary, and this boundary condition leads to a solution for the values of E^s and H^s. These vectors provide complete information about the scattering. Not only does this include the value of C_{sca}, but also the details of the angular distribution and polarization of the scattered radiation. In addition, if absorption takes place, the value of C_{abs} is obtained, so that the same theory describes both scattering and absorption.

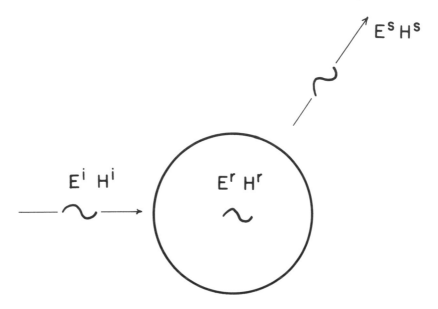

Fig. 4. Scattering theory schematicized. The incident wave is depicted by E^i, H^i; the scattered wave by E^s, H^s; the internal wave by E^r, H^r.

This leads to some interesting effects. The color of a large body is determined by the wavelength dependence of the reflected and absorbed light which in turn is determined by the dispersion of the optical constants. This is also true of small particles except that the wavelength dependence of both the scattering and absorption may be strongly dependent upon particle size and shape as well as upon the optical constants. Accordingly, the same material can appear quite differently for different particle sizes. Faraday (11) was aware of this when he undertook his classic experiments with gold sols. He found that these brilliantly colored stable suspensions took on different ruby and violet hues depending upon how they were prepared. Faraday recognized that the different colors were a consequence of the way in which the metallic gold particles of various sizes "reflected, deflected, transmitted, refracted, absorbed, etc." the light. Also, he clearly described what

we now call the Tyndall effect more than a decade before Tyndall's
(12) investigations of scattering by aerosols.

> *Fluids thus prepared may differ much in*
> *appearance . . . when in their finest state,*
> *(they) often remain unchanged for many*
> *months, and have all the appearance of solutions.*
> *But they never are such, containing in fact*
> *no dissolved, but only diffused gold. The particles*
> *are easily rendered evident, by gathering the*
> *rays of the sun (or a lamp) into a cone by*
> *a lens, and sending the part of the cone near the*
> *focus into the fluid; the cone becomes visible,*
> *and though the illuminated particles cannot*
> *be distinguished because of their minuteness, yet*
> *the light that they reflect is golden in character*
> *and seems to be abundant in proportion to the*
> *quantity of solid gold present.*

Small Particles

Scattering by small particles can be described quite simply,
and there are two cases of particular interest. If the particle
is a transparent sphere, small compared to the wavelength of the
light, a solution proposed by Lord Rayleigh (13) applies. The
cross section is:

$$C_{sca} = \frac{24\pi^3 V^2}{\lambda^4} \left(\frac{m^2 - 1}{m^2 + 2}\right)^2 \qquad \text{(Eq. 3)}$$

and the intensity at a distance r for scattering angle θ is:

$$I = \frac{9\pi^2 V^2}{2r^2\lambda^4} \left(\frac{m^2 - 1}{m^2 + 2}\right)^2 (1 + \cos^2 \theta) \qquad \text{(Eq. 4)}$$

where V is the particle volume, m the refractive index, and λ is
the wavelength. Fig. 5 illustrates how the radiant energy is dis-
tributed in the scattering plane. This is a polar diagram for which
the radius vector to the outer curve is proportional to the radiant
energy scattered in the indicated direction. The inner curves,
designated I and II, show the respective polarized components

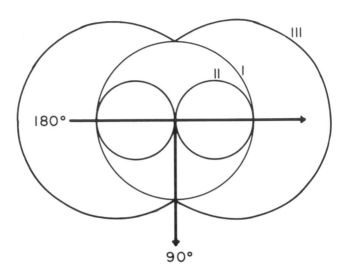

Fig. 5. Radiation pattern for small dielectric spheres (Rayleigh scattering). Curves I and II represent angular intensity for incident light polarized perpendicular and parallel, respectively, to the scattering plane. Curve III, which is the sum of the others, represents the pattern for unpolarized incident light. The intensity of scattered light in any direction is proportional to the radius vector to the curve.

which vibrate perpendicular to the scattering plane and parallel to it.

The important feature of these curves, to which we will draw attention later, is the symmetry about the 90° axis. The radiation scattered into the front half space mirrors exactly that scattered into the back half space. Other aspects of Rayleigh scattering are the complete polarization of the scattered light at 90° and the dependence of the intensity on the inverse fourth power of the wavelength, and on the square of the particle volume. It is the wavelength dependence which accounts for the blue color of the sky as well as the orange of the setting sun.

We will now digress somewhat to consider some consequences of the dependence of the scattering upon the square of the volume. This means that a given amount of material will scatter more intensely when the material is more coarsely divided. This is illustrated in Fig. 6 where branch A of the curve shows how the turbidity (which is the scattering per unit volume) for a fixed amount of material increases with increasing particle size. Indeed, this is the key factor that controls visibility in the atmosphere.

The degradation of atmospheric visibility is due to the presence of a small amount of aerosol which scatters much more intensely than the much smaller air molecules. Moreover, under conditions of high humidity, this condition is aggravated by the condensation of water and consequent increase in size of the particle, giving rise to haze. When the particles are very much larger than the wavelength, the scattering may be thought of as due to geometrical blocking so that the scattering cross section is proportional to the cross-sectional area, in fact:

$$C_{sca} = 2\pi a^2 \qquad (Eq. 5)$$

where a is the particle radius. Since the total cross-sectional area

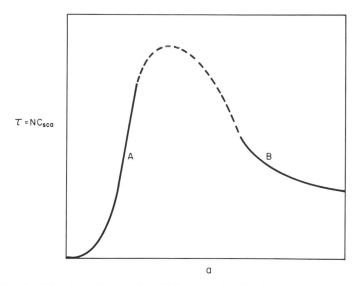

Fig. 6. The dependence of turbidity, τ, of a fixed volume of scattering material upon the particle radius, a. For branch A, $\tau \sim a^3$; for branch B, $\tau \sim a^{-1}$.

for a given amount of material decreases with increasing particle size, the turbidity will also decrease as shown in branch *B* of Fig. 6.

Obviously, there must be an intermediate size range where the scattering by a given amount of material and hence its effect upon the degradation of visibility is maximum. This turns out, not surprisingly, to be at a particle size comparable to the wavelength, or at a radius of about half a micron. We should also not be surprised to learn that smoke particles are in this regime. Indeed, Table I, which compares the scattering power of equal volumes of air, dense smoke, and a medium rain, is rather instructive.

TABLE I
COMPARISON OF TURBIDITY OF AIR, SMOKE, AND RAIN

	Number per ml	Radius (cm)	Density	Turbidity
Air	3×10^{19}	—	1.2×10^{-3}	6×10^{-12}
Smoke	1×10^{7}	5×10^{-5}	5×10^{-6}	2×10^{-1}
Rain	1×10^{-3}	5×10^{-2}	5×10^{-7}	2×10^{-5}

The striking thing is not that smoke is more than ten orders of magnitude more turbid than clear air, for that is a common experience, but that the mass of the smoke which does all this scattering is less than the mass of the air by more than two orders of magnitude. Furthermore, the turbidity of the smoke is four orders of magnitude greater than the rain, although the density of the smoke is only ten times greater. Obviously, a little aerosol goes a long way. No wonder that the effect of aerosol in a polluted atmosphere is so apparent. And no wonder, in view of the minute quantities with which one is dealing, that measurements are so difficult and elusive.

The second limiting case to which we call attention is for a particle, also small compared to the wavelength, but, instead of being transparent, it is composed of a highly reflecting material. The intensity is given by:

$$I = \frac{9\pi^2 V^2}{2r^2\lambda^4} \left[\left(1 - \frac{1}{2}\cos\theta\right)^2 + \left(\cos\theta - \frac{1}{2}\right)^2 \right] \quad \text{(Eq. 6)}$$

and the radiation diagram is now depicted by Fig. 7. The difference between this result and that for small transparent spheres is quite apparent. The scattering is no longer symmetrical about 90°. The preponderance of the scattering is into the back half space; indeed, the scattering directly backward is nine times that scattered directly forward.

When the particle size is comparable to the wave length or larger, the scattering is predominantly in the forward direction. This is true for transparent materials, absorbing materials, or highly reflecting materials, and is illustrated in Fig. 8 which depicts the radiation pattern for a transparent particle whose circumference is five times greater than the wavelength.

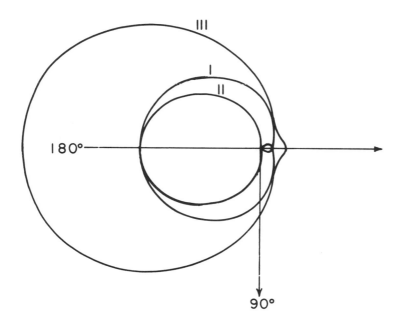

Fig. 7.   Radiation pattern for small perfectly reflecting spheres. See Fig. 5 for description of curves I, II, and III.

Radiation Pressure

It will be useful to characterize the angular distribution of the scattered radiant energy by a quantity called the asymmetry factor for scattering:

$$\langle \cos \theta \rangle_{sca} = \frac{2\pi r^2}{C_{sca}} \int_{-1}^{1} I \cos \theta \, d(\cos \theta) \qquad \text{(Eq. 7)}$$

The integral is proportional to the average value of cos θ with the angular intensity as a weighting factor. The physical meaning can be visualized with the aid of a radiation pattern diagram such as Fig. 8. The radius vector to the curve is proportional to the intensity of the energy scattered in that direction, and, when multiplied by cos θ, this gives its component in the forward direction. Accordingly, if we think of I cos θ as an intensity vector, the asymmetry factor gives the net component returned to the incident direction as a fraction of the total scattered intensity.

For symmetrical scattering such as for a small transparent sphere, where the backscattering is exactly balanced by the forward scattering, $\langle \cos \theta \rangle_{sca} = 0$; when backscattering predominates, as for a small highly reflecting sphere, $\langle \cos \theta \rangle_{sca} < 0$, and for spheres of any material comparable or larger than the wavelength which scatter predominantly into the forward direction, $\langle \cos \theta \rangle_{sca} > 0$.

We now turn to radiation pressure. Although the notion that light carries momentum as well as energy is an old one, it wasn't until Maxwell demonstrated this as a consequence of the electromagnetic theory that it was established on a scientific basis.

The fact that the tails of comets are frequently bent away from the sun was ascribed by Kepler (1619) to a solar force. These comet tails, which may extend for tens of millions of miles, appear to be composed mainly of dust particles which apparently are in the same size range as the aerosol particles of which we have been speaking. It was in order to determine whether these tails might be bent because of the radiation pressure of sunlight that Peter Debye (14), in his 1909 doctoral thesis, derived the theory of radiation pressure on small particles.

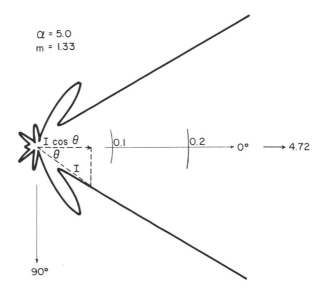

Fig. 8. Radiation pattern for spheres whose circumference is 5 times the wavelength. Refractive index is 1.33. This corresponds to curve I of Fig. 5. $I \cos \theta$ is the component in the incident direction of the radius vector to the curve.

According to Maxwell's theory, the electromagnetic waves carry momentum in the same direction as the energy flow, and this is given by:

$$m = u/c \qquad \text{(Eq. 8)}$$

where u is the energy and c is the velocity of the radiation in the medium. The electromagnetic momentum will manifest itself as a radiation force or pressure whenever the momentum of an incident field is changed by scattering or absorption, and it is this that links the light pressure on a sphere to the phenomenon of light scattering and light absorption.

Debye proposed a relation which can be written as:

$$\frac{1}{c}\left[C_{pr} = C_{ext} - \langle \cos \theta \rangle_{sca} C_{sca} \right] \qquad \text{(Eq. 9)}$$

The quantities on the right-hand side of this equation have already been defined. C_{ext} and C_{sca} are the cross sections for extinction and scattering. They represent the radiant energy removed from the incident beam per unit time by scattering plus absorption and by scattering alone, respectively. The asymmetry factor $\langle\cos\theta\rangle_{sca}$ is the component of the scattered radiation in the forward direction. C_{pr} is called the cross section for radiation pressure. If each term in the equation is divided by the velocity of light, then (C_{ext}/c) represents the momentum per second carried by the incident beam which has been annihilated by virtue of radiant energy being removed from the incident beam by scattering plus absorption. The next term $(\langle\cos\theta\rangle_{sca}\,C_{sca})/c$ represents the momentum per second which is carried back into the forward direction by the scattered radiation. Then, C_{pr}/c represents the net time rate of removal of momentum from the forward direction. In order to conserve momentum, the particle must experience a force in the incident direction equal to this. Units of pressure may be obtained by dividing by the cross-sectional area of the sphere which leads in the standard notation to:

$$\frac{1}{c}\left[Q_{pr} = Q_{ext} - \langle\cos\theta\rangle_{sca}\,Q_{sca}\right] \qquad \text{(Eq. 10)}$$

where Q_{pr}, Q_{ext}, and Q_{sca} are called the efficiencies for radiation pressure, extinction, and scattering. Q_{pr}/c is the radiation pressure.

When the scattering is symmetrical with respect to the forward and backward half spaces, as is the case for small transparent spheres, $\langle\cos\theta\rangle_{sca} = 0$; then $Q_{pr} = Q_{ext}$. In this case the radiation pressure arises from the annihilation of the momentum transported by that part of the incident beam which has been absorbed and /or scattered. For a particle which scatters predominantly into the forward direction, $\langle\cos\theta\rangle_{sca} > 0$ and the radiation pressure will be correspondingly less. In the limit of a scatterer which returns all of the radiation to the forward direction (and, of course, this means that there is no scattering) $\langle\cos\theta\rangle_{sca} = 1$, and there would be no radiation pressure. This limit might appear to be fictitious, but it is conceivable to construct objects with appropriately tailored optical constants which will return all of the radiation into the incident beam and hence will be invisible. If the scattering is predominantly in the backward direction, such as for small spheres composed of a highly reflecting material, $\langle \cos \theta \rangle_{sca} < 0$ and the radiation pressure will be greater than for the symmetrical case. The limit in this instance is a perfect reflector, a body which completely reverses the incident radiation. There is a venerable history among microwave engineers of attempts to construct such devices which are called Luneberg lenses. For such a particle $\langle \cos \theta \rangle_{sca} = -1$, and the radiation pressure:

$$Q_{pr} = Q_{ext} + Q_{sca} = Q_{abs} + 2Q_{sca} \qquad \text{(Eq. 11)}$$

This corresponds to complete reversal of the momentum transported by that part of the incident beam which is scattered plus the annihilation of the momentum transported by that part of the incident beam which is absorbed.

An important point to emphasize is that conservation of momentum requires that the radiation pressure must always be positive, *i.e.,* there can never be a net force in the direction opposite to that of incident beam.

Photophoresis

The term photophoresis was coined by F. Ehrenhaft (15) to describe the effect of light upon the motion of aerosol particles which absorb as well as scatter light. He and others observed that the particles generally moved in the direction of the light beam, but that sometimes the motion was into the beam. The latter was termed negative photophoresis. The effect of electric and magnetic fields, of gas pressure, and of various gaseous media on the photophoretic motions were also studied in some detail.

Photophoresis is quite distinct from radiation pressure. It is due to differential heating of the particle upon the absorption of light in the presence of a fluid medium. The motion arises from a radiometer effect as a result of the interaction of the heated particle surface with the fluid molecules. This can be visualized in Fig. 9 where the shading depicts the local distribution of temperature within the particle as a result of heating by the absorption of part of the radiant energy. In this case the front side of the particle is hotter than the backside. The progression of absorbed energy through the sphere can be envisaged in three steps:

1. Electromagnetic energy is absorbed and reappears as thermal energy. The local distribution of this thermal energy will be referred to as the source function, and this may be quite non-uniform.

2. Heat will flow to the surface of the sphere by thermal conduction.

3. Thermal energy and the associated momentum will be transported from the surface by radiation and in the presence of a fluid medium by conduction and convection.

Now, if the source function is non-uniform, there is the possibility that the steady state temperature at the surface will be non-uniform and in turn the heat loss through the surface and hence the momentum transport will also be non-uniform. Fig. 9 depicts the case for negative photophoresis. The hotter front surface will radiate more intensely. The molecules will rebound from it more energetically. Therefore, in order to conserve momentum, the particle will experience a force which will move it into the light beam—negative photophoresis.

The distinction between photophoresis and thermophoresis should be apparent. Thermophoresis has its origin in a uniformly heated particle placed in a temperature gradient located in the gas. In photophoresis, the gas is at a uniform temperature, whereas the temperature gradient is located within the particle.

The starting point for a theory of photophoresis must be the determination of the source function which describes the local distribution of heat within the particle. This seems to have eluded workers who have heretofore used very crude approximations. For example, a recent definitive review of photophoresis states (16), "Particle size and wavelength are generally of the same magnitude, *so that the heat production cannot be calculated* (our italics), since properties and behavior of materials in such thin layers (for such small particles) are not known."

The matter is hardly that difficult, and we have recently proposed a solution for the source function. We have seen that the scattered electromagnetic field (E^s and H^s) is obtained from the condition that the tangential components of the electromagnetic field vectors be continuous across the surface of the sphere.

This same condition permits us to solve for the electromagnetic field within the sphere (E^r and H^r, see Fig. 4), and from this it is a simple matter to calculate the source function.

The source function is quite complicated and we are now engaged in the rather arduous task of programming it for machine calculation. Then we will attempt to determine the surface temperature distribution in order to calculate the photophoretic force. We believe that by determining the source function, we have found the key to calculating the photophoretic force.

Absorbing Particles

We will now return to a consideration of radiation pressure on particles which absorb as well as scatter light, restricting our considerations to a particle suspended in a vacuum or a highly attenuated atmosphere in order to eliminate the complexities of the dynamic interactions between the heated particle and the gas molecules, as well as the effects of both translational and rotational

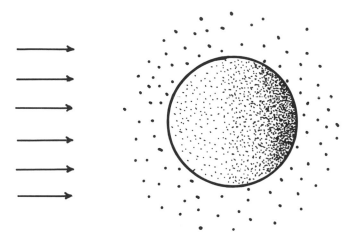

Fig. 9.   Temperature distribution within an illuminated partially absorbing sphere. Darker shading indicates higher temperature. Dots outside the sphere represent gas molecules.

Brownian motion of the particle. It is these interactions which give rise to the radiometer force which results in photophoresis. On the other hand, the force effects which arise in a vacuum, both from scattering and from absorption, are closely related and both of these will be subsumed under the heading of radiation pressure. This will correspond to the problem of particles in space or in the upper atmosphere. Even in the absence of gas, there are quite a number of physical parameters to consider including size, refractivity, optical absorptivity, thermal conductivity, emissivity, wavelength, and intensity of illumination.

Although Debye's expression (equation 9) for radiation pressure contains implicitly within the term, (C_{ext}/c), the rate of *removal* of momentum from the incident beam by absorption as well as by scattering, it is incomplete because it only includes the rate of momentum *returned* to the incident beam by scattering. It ignores the possibility of additional momentum transfer by thermal processes which occur whenever the surface temperature distribution is asymmetric. Accordingly, Debye's equation must be modified by including a term to account for the reradiation of the absorbed energy as follows:

$$\frac{1}{c}\left[C_{pr} = C_{ext} - \langle\cos\theta\rangle_{sca}\, C_{sca} - \langle\cos\theta\rangle_{abs}\, C_{abs} \right] \qquad \text{(Eq. 12)}$$

or

$$\frac{1}{c}\left[C_{pr} = (C_{sca} - \langle\cos\theta\rangle_{sca}\, C_{sca}) + (C_{abs} - \langle\cos\theta\rangle_{abs}\, C_{abs}) \right]$$

$$\text{(Eq. 13)}$$

We call $\langle\cos\theta\rangle_{abs}$ the asymmetry factor for absorption. It describes the fractional net rate of return of momentum to the incident direction as a result of the momentum transfer originating in the heating of the particle by the absorption of radiant energy. In a vacuum this will be thermal radiation. The expression $(C_{abs} - \langle\cos\theta\rangle_{abs}\, C_{abs})/c$ is the force derived from the removal of momentum from the incident beam by absorption combined with that restored to the incident beam by radiation.

Each of the comments made earlier about $\langle\cos\theta\rangle_{sca}$ applies equally to $\langle\cos\theta\rangle_{abs}$. When the temperature distribution is uniform, $\langle \cos \theta \rangle_{abs} = 0$, and there will be no net force due to momentum transfer by radiation. When the back surface is hotter, $\langle \cos \theta \rangle_{abs}$ falls between 0 and -1, and this will result in a force which will enhance that due to the extinction of the incident beam. When the front surface is hotter, $\langle \cos \theta \rangle_{abs}$ falls between 0 and 1, and the force on the particle will be correspondingly reduced. However, in a vacuum, there can never be a motion corresponding to negative photophoresis—a resultant movement opposed to the light beam—since the momentum transferred into the forward direction by thermal radiation from the front side of the particle is always counterbalanced by the disappearance of an amount of momentum in the incident beam corresponding to all of the absorbed energy. Thus each grouping in equation 12 must always be positive:

$$C_{sca} - \langle \cos \theta \rangle_{sca} \, C_{sca} \geq 0 \qquad \text{(Eq. 14)}$$

$$C_{abs} - \langle \cos \theta \rangle_{abs} \, C_{abs} \geq 0 \qquad \text{(Eq. 15)}$$

Indeed, it seems that in the light of this discussion, at least in a vacuum, there is little reason to distinguish between radiation pressure which has its origin in scattering and that originating in absorption. The expression in equation 14 gives the contribution to radiation pressure which arises from scattering, whereas that in equation 15 gives the contribution from absorption.

The values of C_{sca} and C_{abs} are not unrelated to each other. The fraction of energy lost from the incident beam by scattering, called the albedo, is given by:

$$A = \frac{C_{sca}}{C_{sca} + C_{abs}} = \frac{C_{sca}}{C_{ext}} \qquad \text{(Eq. 16)}$$

The dependence of the albedo upon particle size and upon complex refractive index is shown in Fig. 10. The two values chosen correspond to a typically metallic material (1.29-0.472i) and to a highly colored dielectric (1.29-0.0472i). For sufficiently large particles the scattering and absorption cross sections are approximately equal.

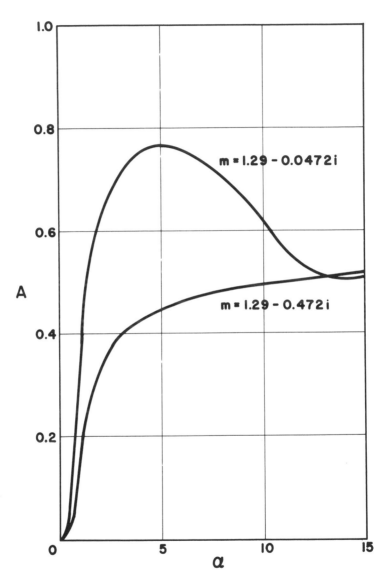

Fig. 10. Albedo (fraction of extinction which is comprised of scattered radiation) as a function of particle size ($\alpha = 2\pi a/\lambda$ where a is radius and λ is wavelength) for slightly absorbing ($m = 1.29$-$0.0472\ i$) and highly absorbing ($m = 1.29$-$0.472\ i$) spheres.

Radiation Pressure and the Radiometer Effect

We have seen how in a vacuum a particle may experience a radiation pressure which is due on the one hand to scattering and on the other to absorption with subsequent reradiation of the thermal energy. It is a relatively simple matter in this case to determine the momentum balance once the energy distribution is known. Momentum is obtained from radiant energy simply by dividing by the velocity of light. The force on the particle arises from the difference between the rate of momentum transport by the incident beam and that by the scattered and reradiated energy.

In the presence of a gas the redistribution of the momentum related to the absorption is more complex giving rise to the radiometer force. Now the absorbed energy is carried away from the particle by the gas molecules which impinge upon the particle surface, sit upon the surface for a short time acquiring some excess energy, and then rebound from the surface with a greater velocity on the average than they possessed upon impingement.

That the radiometer effect becomes dominant at ordinary pressures can be illustrated by the following crude calculation. For a gas at standard conditions and for a light beam of usual laboratory intensity an estimate of the energy balance is given by:

$$\frac{1}{2} F m \Delta v^2 = E \qquad \text{(Eq. 17)}$$

where F is the flux of gas molecules to the particle surface, m is the molecular mass, Δv^2 is the increase in the square of the molecular velocity, and E is the rate of energy transport. If one now determines from this equation the increase of the molecular velocity and in turn the increase in momentum, one finds that the momentum transported by the molecules is many orders of magnitude greater than the momentum obtained if the same amount of energy had been transported away from the particle by reradiation, i.e.:

$$F m \Delta v \gg \frac{E}{c} \qquad \text{(Eq. 18)}$$

In order to conserve momentum, the particle itself must experience a corresponding change in momentum and it is this which comprises the radiometric force.

It follows then that if the particle is unevenly heated and if the energy and momentum transport is primarily by molecular conduction and convection rather than by radiation, the particle will experience a radiometric force which is much greater than that due to radiation pressure alone.

It is this particular phenomenon, where the radiometric force arises from the absorption of light, which is called photophoresis. It may turn out, as in the case illustrated in Fig. 9, that the front side of the particle becomes hotter, and then the radiometric force will propel the particle back into the light beam, giving rise to negative photophoresis. Of course, such negative movement can never occur in a vacuum where radiation pressure predominates.

With our present solution of the source function which describes the local generation of heat within the particle, it now becomes possible to make precise calculations of the radiometric forces which prevail in photophoresis. We are currently performing these calculations.

Radiation Pressure in Nature and in the Laboratory

Radiation pressure figures importantly in the economy of dust particles in the universe and particularly within the solar system. Possible sources of the interplanetary dust, which is presumed to be in heliocentric orbit, are the comets, debris from asteroidal collisions, an interstellar cloud through which the solar system may be passing, or the residue of an original dust cloud which may have been much denser. Much of our knowledge of this dust is based upon observation of scattered sunlight—the zodiacal light which is a luminous region in the sky seen in the west after sunset or in the east before sunrise. This has been supplemented in recent years by upper atmosphere and space probes as well as by studies of radioaluminum in the ocean sediment.

The interplanetary particles are effected in two ways. Radiation pressure supplements the centrifugal force of the orbiting particles, and for particles smaller than about a tenth of a micron, it is great enough to result in their ultimate ejection from the solar system. There is also the Poynting-Robertson effect (17) which causes a tangential drag on an orbiting particle and in turn this reduces the angular momentum and makes the particle spiral into the sun. As a result, dust particles from the outer planetary system are continuously crossing the earth's orbit where they may be captured and form a dust blanket orbiting the earth. It is estimated that about 1000 tons a day of this falls to earth.

There have been very few laboratory studies. Radiation pressure was demonstrated experimentally by P. N. Lebedev, E. F. Nichols, and G. F. Hull around the turn of the century. Hull's experiment (18) was particularly ingenious for the manner in which it eliminated the radiometer effect. The apparatus consisted of a vane suspended in a sensitive torsion balance maintained at reduced pressure. Fig. 11 is a side view of the two disc-shaped cells of which the vane was comprised. It could be disposed so that the light fell on the silvered or the blackened

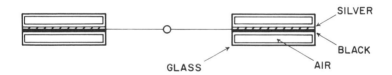

Fig. 11.   The vane in Hull's equipment for measuring light pressure (18). Two glass plates (one silvered and one blackened) back-to-back enclosed in a cell containing an air space.

surface. In either case, the temperature at each outer glass surface was about the same, resulting in cancellation of the radiometer effect. Hull found that the ratio of the deflections obtained when the silvered and blackened surfaces were illuminated in succession agreed closely with the calculated ratio.

It is only recently that radiation pressure has been observed upon small particles by Ashkin (19) who utilized a focused beam of laser light to levitate 20 micron glass spheres in a gravitational field such as shown in Fig. 12. Although there was no attempt at a quantitative analysis, this demonstration certainly dramatizes the existence of radiation pressure. In other experiments with micron-

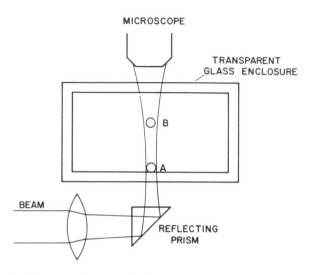

Fig. 12. Ashkin's experiment (19) demonstrating levitation of glass sphere
by light pressure.

size polystyrene latex spheres in water, good agreement was obtained between the measured and calculated terminal velocities
attained by the latex particles when the acceleration due to the
radiation pressure was just compensated by the viscous drag.
Ashkin points to the possibility of using radiation pressure to accelerate micron particles in a vacuum to fantastic velocities such as
3×10^8 centimeters per second. Such a particle, upon impact,
would form a plasma whose temperature would be 50 times higher
than the temperatures needed for thermonuclear reactions.

We have given some thought to an experiment which in its
first stages could be used for a quantitative study of radiation pressure on small particles and ultimately might provide a tool for the
study of the aerodynamics of such particles. The apparatus is
depicted schematically in Fig. 13. It consists of three parts—(a) a
vibrating orifice generator which produces a beam of aerosol
particles, (b) an evacuated column containing a system of baffles
which collimates the areosol beam and an intense laser beam which
deflects the areosol beam, and (c) a detection system which measures the deflection.

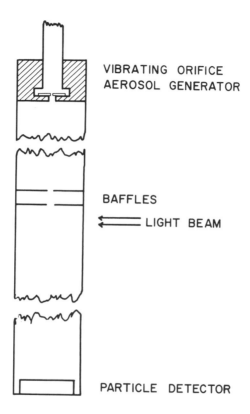

VIBRATING ORIFICE
AEROSOL GENERATOR

BAFFLES

LIGHT BEAM

PARTICLE DETECTOR

Fig. 13.   Proposed experiment for measuring deflection of an aerosol beam
in vacuum by light pressure.

The vibrating orifice generator such as the one described by
Bergland and Liu (20) is based upon the breakup of a liquid jet
into uniform-size droplets when subjected to a periodic vibration.
In practice, the generator can produce a stream of droplets with
radii as small as 5 microns moving at a velocity of about 50 meters
per second. Smaller particles can be obtained by utilizing a dispersion of these in a volatile solvent which will evaporate in the
evacuated column. The particles will experience the radiation force
on passing through the light beam and will accelerate to a particular velocity which will persist until they reach the particle

detector, which will record the magnitude of the deflection. This is
given by:

$$d = \frac{bt}{v_1 m} \frac{C_{pr}}{c} I_0 \qquad \text{(Eq. 19)}$$

where b is the height of the light beam, v_1 is the vertical velocity of
the particle at the light beam, t is the time of fall from the light
beam to the particle detector, m is the mass of the particle, c is
the velocity of light, C_{pr} is the cross section for radiation pressure,
and I_0 is the light intensity. A beam of 0.2-micron polystyrene
spheres in a 5-meter column would be deflected a centimeter by a
20-watt laser beam focused down to a 0.1-mm diameter. Such a
deflection could be precisely measured.

This apparatus offers the possibility of studying, in addition
to non-absorbing spheres, the radiation pressure on absorbing
spheres where the radiometer effect is present, as well as the
radiation pressure on non-spherical particles. It could also serve
as a particle size analyzer. Furthermore, by conducting experiments in the presence of gas both at reduced pressure and at
elevated pressure, the motion of small particles under impulsion
by precisely known forces could be readily studied in aerodynamic
regimes not presently accessible.

REFERENCES

1. Robert Brown, 'A brief account of microscopical observations made in
   the months of June, July, and August, 1827 on the particles contained
   in the pollen of plants; and on the general existence of active molecules
   in organic and inorganic bodies,' *Phil. Mag.,* **4,** 161 (1828).
2. Richard Zsigmondy, "Zur Erkenntnis der Kolloide," G. Fischer, Jena,
   1905. English translation by Jerome Alexander, "Colloids and the
   Ultramicroscope," John Wiley, New York, 1909.
3. Norbert Wiener, 'The average of an analytical function and the
   Brownian movement,' *Proc. Natl. Acad. Sci. U.S.A.,* **7,** 294 (1921).
4. Albert Einstein, 'On the kinetic molecular theory of thermal movements
   of particles suspended in a quiescent fluid,' *Ann. Physik,* **17,** 549 (1905).
   English translation by A. D. Cowper in "Investigations on the Theory
   of the Brownian Movement," by Albert Einstein, edited by R. Fürth,
   Dover Publications, New York, 1956.
5. N. A. Fuchs, "The Mechanics of Aerosols," MacMillan, New York,
   1964.
6. Milton Kerker and Derry D. Cooke, 'Radiation pressure on absorbing
   spheres and photophoresis,' *Applied Optics,* **12,** 1377 (1973).

7. Milton Kerker, "The Scattering of Light and Other Electromagnetic Radiation," Academic Press, New York, 1969.
8. John W. Strutt (Lord Rayleigh), 'On the electromagnetic theory of light,' *Phil. Mag.,* **12,** 81 (1881).
9. Ludwig Lorenz, 'On the light reflected and refracted by a transparent sphere,' *Vidensk. Selsk. Skrifter,* **6,** 1 (1890). Also, "Oeuvres Scientifiques de L. Lorenz," Vol. 1, Copenhagen: Librairie Lehmann 1896, pp. 405-502 (Reprinted, Johnson, 1964).
10. Gustav Mie, 'Contributions to the optics of turbid media, specially colloidal metal sols,' *Ann. Physik,* **25,** 377 (1908).
11. Michael Faraday, 'Experimental relations of gold (and other metals) to light,' *Phil. Trans.,* **147,** 145 (1857).
12. John Tyndall, 'On the blue colour of the sky, the polarization of skylight and on the polarization of light by cloudy matter generally,' *Phil. Mag.,* **37,** 384 (1869); 'Note on the formation and phenomena of clouds,' *Phil. Mag.,* **38,** 156 (1869).
13. John W. Strutt (Lord Rayleigh), 'On the light from the sky, its polarization and colour,' *Phil. Mag.,* **41,** 107 and 274 (1871). Also, *Scientific Papers,* **1,** 87 (1899).
14. P. Debye, 'Light pressure on spheres of any material,' *Ann. Physik,* **30,** 57 (1909).
15. Felix Ehrenhaft, 'Towards a physics of millionths of centimeters,' *Physik Zeitschr.,* **17,** 352 (1917).
16. Othmar Preining in "Aerosol Science," C. N. Davies, editor, Academic Press, London, 1966, pp. 111-135.
17. J. H. Poynting, 'Radiation in the solar system; its effects on temperature and its effect on small bodies,' *Phil. Trans.* **A202,** 525 (1903); H. P. Robertson, 'Dynamical effects of radiation in the solar system,' *Mon. Not. Roy. Astron. Soc.,* **97,** 423 (1937).
18. G. F. Hull, 'The elimination of gas action in experiments on light pressure,' *Phys. Rev.,* **20,** 292 (1905). Also, E. F. Nichols and G. F. Hull, 'A preliminary communication on the pressure of heat and light radiation,' *Phys. Rev.,* **13,** 307 (1901).
19. Arthur Ashkin, 'Acceleration and trapping of particles by radiation pressure,' *Phys. Rev. Letters,* **24,** 156 (1970); 'The pressure of laser light,' *Sci. Amer.,* **226,** 63 (1972); Arthur Ashkin and J. M. Dziedzic, 'Optical levitation by radiation pressure,' *Appl. Phys. Letters,* **19,** 283 (1971).
20. Richard N. Berglund and Benjamin Y. H. Liu, 'Generation of monodisperse aerosol standards,' *Environmental Sci. and Technol.,* **7,** 147 (1973).

How Psychological Factors Can Affect Visceral Functions

By Neal E. Miller*

* Professor of Psychology and Head of Laboratory of Physiological Psychology, the Rockefeller University

I am pleased and honored to have been invited to participate in this event. Seeing this fine research building is indeed encouraging to me. We live in a time when some of our great American industries are losing their technological superiority because they are not investing enough money in research, engineering, and development. Therefore, it is particularly encouraging to see the investment that is being made by this company in the area of research. It comes at a time when some people are disparaging the search for new knowledge for its own sake. But as Lord Todd pointed out earlier in his brilliant historical summary of the development of his field, discoveries which do not seem to be immediately related to any practical problem often turn out in the long run to have the greatest practical implications. I am glad that he has reminded us of this important lesson from the history of science and industrial development.

*   *   *   *   *   *

Psychological Factors in Stress-produced Effects

How can psychological factors modify visceral responses? Fig. 1 shows two ways. In a danger situation, particularly in a situation of intermittent danger, learning can affect the amount and duration of an emotion such as fear that is induced. Then the emotion can directly and physiologically produce an effect such as an increased heart rate—where the heart beats madly with fear—or the opposite effect of a decreased heart rate—when the heart stands still in fear. Similarly, as our first experiments are going to show, one of the direct effects of strong emotion can be lesions in the stomach. Clinical observations over a long period of time have suggested that psychological factors can be important in a great number of psychosomatic symptoms such as stomach lesions, but it is difficult to use such clinical observations unequivocally to prove the point.

One of my students and associates, Dr. Weiss, has tried to study the problem more rigorously. Two rats, as illustrated in Fig. 2, had electrodes on their tails wired in series, so that each gets physically exactly the same electric shock as the other. They were in different soundproof compartments, semi-restrained. One rat received a signal which immediately preceded the electric shock; the other rat received the same signal, but uncorrelated with the shock. Thus, one rat had the opportunity to know when it would be dangerous and when it would be safe, while the other rat did not. A third rat was the lucky control which didn't get any shocks at all.

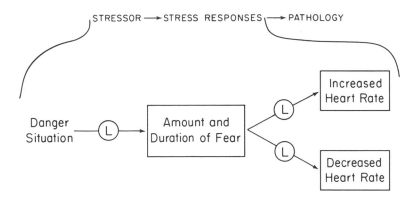

Fig. 1. Two different ways in which learning may affect a psychosomatic symptom: (a) it may affect the amount and duration of an emotional response such as fear, which in turn may have a direct innate tendency to produce psychosomatic change; and (b) it may affect the type and amount of visceral response that is elicited in response to a given emotional state. From *Seminars in Psychiatry,* **4,** 239 (1972). © 1972 by Grune & Stratton, Inc. Reprinted by permission.

Fig. 3 shows the average length of stomach lesions produced in this experiment. The non-shock rats which were semi-restrained without any food for a period of time suffered only a few lesions. The rats which received a signal so they could learn when it was dangerous and when it was safe suffered slightly more stomach lesions. However, the unsignaled rats which had no opportunity to learn when it was dangerous and when it was safe had far more stomach lesions. They also ate less outside of the experimental situation, lost more weight, had higher levels of plasma corticosterone, and indicated other symptoms of distress. The large differences must have been the result of purely psychological variables, since both the signaled and the unsignaled rats received exactly the same physical amount of electric shock.

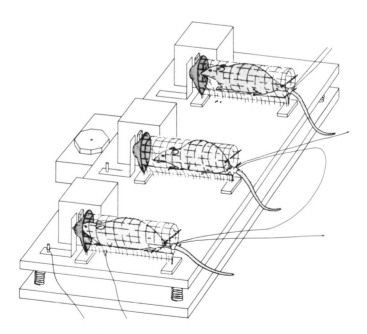

Fig. 2. Apparatus for studying psychological factors affecting psychosomatic effects of shocks that are equally strong because the electrodes on the tails of the two yoked animals are wired in series. From *J. Comp. Physiol. Psychol.*, **65**, 251 (1968). © 1968 by the American Psychological Association. Reprinted by permission.

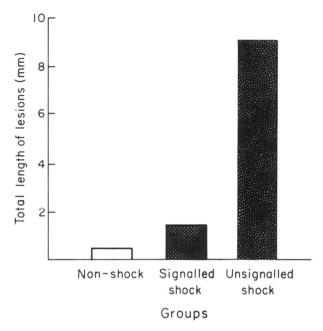

Fig. 3. The amount of stomach lesions that are produced by signaled (predictable) as compared with unsignaled (unpredictable) electric shocks of equal physical intensity. From *Seminars in Psychiatry,* **4,** 239 (1972). © 1972 by Grune & Stratton, Inc. Reprinted by permission.

Another experiment used the same apparatus but with a small modification. One rat could perform the very simple response of poking his nose out and touching a metal plate to actuate an electronic relay and turn off the shock, or if he acted in time, to avoid it. Another rat got exactly the same shocks, he could perform the same act, but the metal plate was not connected to anything, so that he was at the mercy of his stupid partner. A third rat was the lucky control rat which received no shocks.

Fig. 4 demonstrates the effect of being able to perform a coping response that exerts control over the situation. The animal that controlled the situation—he has sometimes been called the executive rat—had somewhat more stomach lesions than the non-shock rat. But the yoked rat that was helpless and at the mercy of his stupid partner got much more stomach lesions. So again, a psychological variable, being able to do something simple and clear-cut about a situation makes a considerable difference. These results agree with clinical observations. During World War II, for example, it was the co-pilots—who had to sit there in dangerous situations while the pilots were flying the planes—who seemed to suffer far more combat fatigue than the pilots.

It is possible, however, for the opposite result to occur, namely, where an executive monkey can get more stomach lesions than his yoked partner. This kind of result was observed by Brady. You may think that this is a species difference (it is easier to be an executive, provided you are a rat), but this is not really the case. If you give the animal a difficult and conflict-inducing task

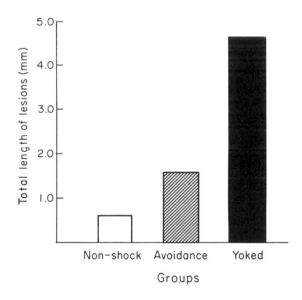

Fig. 4.   The effect of being able to perform an avoidance-coping response on the amount of stomach lesions. Each yoked rat received exactly the same electric shocks as his avoidance partner, because the electrodes on their tails were wired in series. From *Seminars in Psychiatry*, **4**, 239 (1972). © 1972 by Grune & Stratton, Inc. Reprinted by permission.

(for example, by giving the rat a shock for performing the response necessary to turn off the longer series of shocks), it will experience a "devil-and-the-deep-blue-sea" or "Scylla-and-Charybdis" type of problem, which we refer to as an avoidance-avoidance conflict. Fig. 5 shows the kind of results this situation produces. When conflict was introduced into the task, the executive rat developed the most lesions of all—much more than the yoked control which received exactly the same shocks. Consequently, the nature of the task to be performed, whether it is simple and clear-cut or conflict-inducing determines whether being in the executive position is an advantage or a disadvantage. Whenever, as in these experiments, a change in the experimental situation alters the pattern of results, one must be cautious about over-generalizing. Such results show

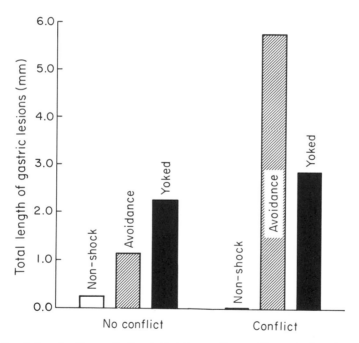

Fig. 5. Being the "executive" rat that learns the avoidance task reduces the amount of stomach lesions when the task is simple and clear-cut, but increases it when the task involves conflict. From *Seminars in Psychiatry,* **4,** 239 (1972). © 1972 by Grune & Stratton, Inc. Reprinted by permission.

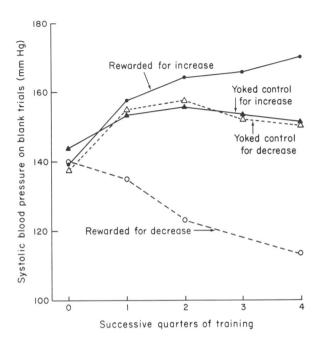

Fig. 6. Changes in blood pressure in experimental and yoked control groups during training. From *Psychosom. Med.*, **30**, 489 (1968). © 1968 by the American Psychosomatic Society. Reprinted by permission.

the importance of studying scientifically and in more detail all of the variables involved. Therefore, I don't want to generalize too widely from these results. Still, one generalization is perfectly clear: namely, that psychological factors such as the ability to learn when it's dangerous and when it's safe and the kind of task one has to perform can make a great difference in the level of stress and in the psychosomatic symptoms that are produced by that stress.

Controlling and Learning Autonomic Responses

Thus far, we have been discussing the effect of psychological variables, such as learning, on the strength of the emotion produced by a stressful situation, as illustrated in the left-hand side of Fig. 1. Now let us look at the right-hand side of Fig. 1 and consider whether in a given emotional situation learning can modify the visceral response produced. It has been believed that the more sophisticated type of learning that occurs by reward and punishment—as opposed to simple learning by classical conditioning—cannot modify responses that are controlled by the autonomic nervous system. It is believed that the autonomic nervous system is fundamentally "more stupid" than the somatic nervous system which controls the skeletal muscles of your arms and legs. But yet in the highest levels of the brain, the cortex, the visceral organs are represented in both sensory and motor functions; this has been known for over 20 years. Therefore, I doubted that this kind of learning was impossible.

If I were to offer you a hundred dollars to speed up your

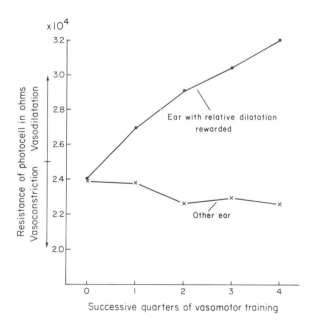

Fig. 7. Learning a difference in the vasomotor responses of two ears in the curarized rat. From *Science*, **163** (No. 3866), 434 (1969). © 1969 by the American Association for the Advancement of Science. Reprinted by permission.

heart, you probably would think for a minute, run up a flight of stairs, come back, and try to collect your money. From my point of view, that would be cheating. It would have demonstrated voluntary control over your arms and legs and as a result of their activity, an *indirect* influence on your heart rate. In order to try partially to control such factors, we used a drug, curare, which paralyzes the skeletal muscles and has considerably less (though perhaps some) effect on the autonomic nervous system. But what kinds of rewards and punishments can you use to train a rat paralyzed by curare so that he has to be maintained on artificial respiration? In some experiments we used electrical stimulation of reward-producing areas of the brain; in other cases we used escape from mild electric shocks to the tail.

Fig. 6 illustrates a typical experiment on rats paralyzed by curare. The day before the experiment, under surgical anaesthesia, each rat had a chronic catheter inserted into his abdominal aorta, so that we could measure his blood pressure on a moment-to-moment basis. The rats were rewarded by escape from, and avoidance of, mild electric shock. Some rats were rewarded for increases in blood pressure. After they had learned to increase a certain amount, we shaped them by progressively requiring larger and larger increases. To other rats we gave similar rewards for learning how to decrease blood pressure. It is evident that these two groups did learn—one how to increase and the other how to decrease—blood pressure. To ensure that these opposite effects were not a result of the number or pattern of shocks, each rat had a yoked partner who got exactly the same shocks, but unrelated to what his blood pressure was doing. It is not surprising that blood pressure increased in both of the yoked groups. However, there was no difference between the two control groups; that is, the yoked rats paired with the experimental animals trained to increase showed the same trend as the yoked rats paired with the experimental animals trained to decrease. So it's hard to explain these effects on the basis of the mere shocks. In these experiments the heart rate did not change. The fact that the change was specific to the type of response that was rewarded, namely blood pressure, was a further control. If the animal were achieving blood pressure fluctuations through indirect means (for example, by commanding his paralyzed muscles to struggle or to relax), one would think that such a mechanism would alter also heart rate, either by classical conditioning or by the innate wiring diagram of the rat.

We have produced the kind of learning illustrated by the foregoing experiment in a variety of visceral responses: heart rate, intestinal contractions, the rate of formation of urine by kidneys, and vasomotor responses. In all of these cases the learning is specific to the type of response that was rewarded. In one such case, as shown in Fig. 7, we pushed the specificity to an extreme by rewarding the achievement of a difference in the amount of blood in the capillaries of the two ears, as measured by photoelectric transducers attached to each ear. To our surprise and delight, the experiment worked. It is hard to imagine any commands to skeletal muscles, or even any emotional thought, that would cause the rat to blush, so to speak, in one ear but not the other.

Our research was going along very well, but as sometimes happens in research (and often doesn't get reported in the results which are written up with wisdom of hindsight), we ran into difficulties while attempting to study new types of visceral responses and to make pharmacological and other analyses of the mechanisms involved. This occurred at a time when there was a turnover in students. The new student was not getting very good results; in fact, he was not getting any learning at all. The earlier experiments had been done by six different students, and so the first thought of some of the earlier students was that the new student was stupid. In order to defend himself, he looked back over what had been happening for the preceding several years and he found the surprising results graphically illustrated in Fig. 8. The effect had been running progressively downhill from year to year, until it was at the point where we were getting no effect. As Fig. 8 shows Brener and Hahn had been getting results similar to those we were securing at the same time, but poorer than our original results. Since then, Brener has had difficulty in replicating his earlier experiment.

We have performed a great number of experiments trying to discover what has happened, but so far we have no explanation. Often there are only one or two ways of doing something right and a million or more ways of doing it wrong. Thus, once you have lost a phenomenon, it's hard to tell exactly what has changed. There are many possibilities. One is that we have been done in by the National Institutes of Health's regulations for animal care. The animals are now being brought up under far softer conditions than they used to be. We are currently testing the possibility that this is the problem by having a "boot-training camp" to toughen up the autonomic nervous systems of our rats. It seems, perhaps, to be producing good results. Nevertheless, we have thought that we were on the right track a number of times before, only to find ourselves victims of the fact that if you run about 2000 rats in experiments trying to find out what was wrong, every once in a

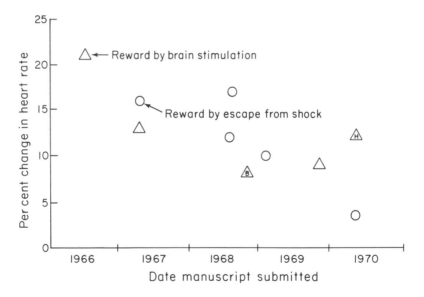

Fig. 8. Progressive decline in amount of learned change in heart rate during a five-year period. Experiments are performed under approximately similar conditions in the author's laboratory, except for point B, which is from data by Hothersall and Brener and point H, which is from data by Slaughter *et al.* For each experiment the increases and decreases are converted to percentage changes and then averaged. From *Seminars in Phychiatry,* **4,** 239 (1972). © 1972 by Grune & Stratton, Inc. Reprinted by permission.

while you will get a run of results that you would expect less than one time in a hundred by chance. So I want to be cautious about concluding that our boot-training camp is solving the problem. It remains a puzzle.

Since I first reported the mysterious decline in our results, quite a number of people have come up to me after talks like this and said, "I'm running into exactly the same kind of problem." One scientist, Dr. Gorski, told me that the amount of male hormone necessary to sterilize a neonatal female rat is now several times greater than it was when he started his work 12 years ago. He thought that his students were just clumsy oafs and weren't administering the hormone correctly, until he repeated the experiment himself and got the same results (which, of course, completely eliminated the clumsy-oaf hypothesis). Another former colleague of mine has had similar results in studies on aggressiveness in a strain of fighting fish. There have been some other cases. Dr. Corner, Executive Officer of the American Philosophical Society, told me he was unable to replicate the results of his colleague Allen in early studies on progesterone with rabbits. By going through their procedures with meticulous detail, they discovered that whereas Allen would usually choose large rabbits out of a group, Corner liked to pick out nice small ones. It just happened that the rabbits were on the borderline of adolescence, so that the hormone they were isolating would work on the big rabbits, but not the small ones. That one peculiar little detail took them quite a while to discover.

Human Evidence

You are probably most interested in whether anything can be done with human subjects. While we have been worried about the perplexing decline in the visceral learning of our animals, paradoxically enough the human evidence has been getting better. There is one visceral response that I trust all of you have learned to control because it doesn't need any elaborate instrumentation to give you knowledge of results and you have considerable motivation to control it; that response is urination, which presumably is controlled entirely by the autonomic nervous system. There has been some debate over whether urination could be controlled indirectly *via* skeletal muscles—say, for example, by tensing the muscles of the body wall so as to increase pressure on the bladder and hence to initiate reflex emptying. A while back Lapides performed an heroic experiment which didn't come to my attention until recently because of the compartmentalization of the literature and of our reading habits. He completely paralyzed 16 subjects (presumably medical students)—half of them by curare and half of them by succinylcholine. The subjects were maintained on artificial respiration. They did not become incontinent—a finding in line with experience in the use of curare in treating tetanus. Lapides found that on command the subjects could start urinating as fast as they could when their skeletal muscles were not paralyzed; they could stop urinating in about 10 seconds (five seconds would be a normal stopping time). Furthermore, he catheterized them and found that the bladders still had plenty of urine left. I think this study demonstrates conclusively that urination is at least one response in which performance can be controlled when the skeletal musculature is completely ruled out by curarization.

Other investigators have been performing experiments on heart rate, blood pressure, vasomotor responses, and galvanic skin responses of human subjects. Here, it is hard to rule out completely subtle effects of respiration and other skeletal responses, since the subjects are not paralyzed and maintained on artificial respiration. For example, you can exert some control over your heart rate by changing the depth or rate of your breathing. However, at Harvard, Shapiro and his group have taught some human subjects to change their blood pressure (to be sure, only a small amount—about five mm) without changing the heart rate, or to change the heart rate (say by five or 10%) without changing their blood pressure. It is hard to explain such effects by skeletal responses such as breathing, which in general change both heart rate and blood pressure together.

Perhaps the most convincing experiment was one designed by Zimbardo to parallel our study of the rat's two ears. In this case he had hypnotized subjects change the temperature of the two hands independently. Fig. 9 shows that these subjects could produce a difference between the two hands which on the average reached a peak of 4°C. Interestingly enough, waking controls were not able to change their temperature as much. Some of these subjects changed the temperature of one hand in one direction and the other hand in the other direction. It is hard to imagine how such changes could be produced by any artifacts, such as hyperventilation. Since then, Roberts, Kewman, and Macdonald, working with Hilgard, have found that by giving hypnotized subjects the opportunity to learn, they can progressively increase the degree of control to as much as 8°C difference between the two hands.

One mechanism by which rats could have achieved the results observed in the two-ears experiment would be by imagery. Indeed, at least some of the hypnotized subjects used this method to control the temperatures of their hands. They imagined that one hand was in hot water and the other in cold. The response of the hand,

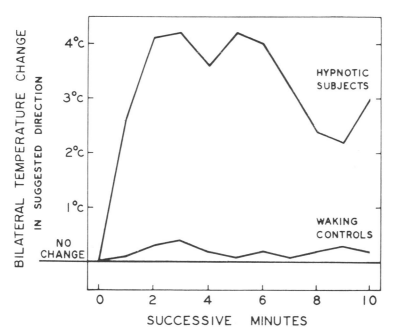

Fig. 9. Achievement of temperature changes between the two hands of hypnotized subjects, according to data from experiments by Zimbardo *et al.* From *Psychophysiology,* **9,** 600 (1972). © 1972 by the Society for Psychophysiological Research. Reprinted by permission of Dr. Philip G. Zimbardo.

if it actually *were* hot, would be vasodilatation—more blood going into the hand—while the response of a cold hand would be vasoconstriction—less blood entering the hand. More blood would raise the hand's temperature, while less blood would lower it. Other subjects claim that they do not use imagery. Of course, it is hard to be certain since we can't look into their minds to find out exactly what they are doing. But there does seem to be evidence that some people *can* control certain visceral responses.

Anand in India has studied Yogis. Some of these use tricks. One of these is called the Valsalva maneuver, which is accomplished as follows. Take a deep breath, close your windpipe, and blow out. With your windpipe closed you can compress the air to produce pressure in your thoracic cavity. If you carry this far enough, you collapse the veins that are bringing blood back to the heart, because that blood is under relatively low pressure. Then, because your heart doesn't have any blood to pump, your pulse disappears, producing the illusion that you have stopped your heart. Of course, people can do this for only short periods of time, say half a minute or so. However, Anand, who is a very good physiologist, has studied other Yogis and found a very few who can apparently genuinely slow down their heart beat as measured by the electrocardiograph. (Electrocardiograms of people using the Valsalva maneuver indicate their hearts are beating faster than ever, as if frantically trying to circulate the blood that isn't there.) He has also discovered two Yogis who can reduce their rates of basal metabolism quite a bit below what has been thought to be normal levels.

Clinical Significance

The evidence strongly suggests that people can, at least in some circumstances, learn some degree of control over certain visceral functions. The next question is whether they can produce enough control to be of clinical significance, and here I think we have to suspend our judgment. It is clear that there are considerable individual differences in the degree of control. Some people, so to speak, are autonomic athletes and some people are autonomic duffers. These individual differences provide an interesting area for further study.

Quite naturally, people who have tried to find clinical applications of something entirely new like visceral learning have tried first to see if they can get any effect at all. We have learned by bitter experience that it is useless to set up elaborate and time-consuming control experiments, only to find that you have no main effect and therefore nothing at all to control for. Unfortunately, some preliminary reports that suggest the possibility of therapeutically useful effects have reached the press, where they have been greatly exaggerated. Such stories fail to indicate the caution with which the experimenter reports his work. Therefore, they produce impossibly high expectations which inevitably lead to disillusionment. I fear that such a reaction will interfere with the large amount of hard work necessary to discover if anything of clinical value is to come out of this line of research.

I am sure that you are aware of the placebo effect: give people a fancy-colored sugar pill and many of them will report that they feel better; in some cases they actually will *be* better for a while. Often there is a cynical comment made to the announcement of a new drug: "You better give it to your patients in a hurry while it's still effective." Some of the symptoms for which people report relief from using visceral training (also called "biofeedback")—*e.g.,* migraine headaches—are just the kind of symptoms that are peculiarly subject to placebo effects. It is known that the migraine headaches of patients often improve when they get a new doctor, whoever the doctor is. But after a while the headaches seem to get worse again, so they go on to another doctor or try some other form of treatment, then get temporary relief, and then repeat this pattern again. One has to be very, very careful of such placebo effects in trying to check on possible clinical applications of this kind of work.

Alpha-wave training has attracted a lot of publicity recently. I have little doubt that people can learn in one way or another to control their brain waves, or at least certain aspects of them. The only question is whether this is of any more value to them than learning to wiggle their ears. I am *not* saying that it certainly is not of value; all I am saying is that alpha-wave training hasn't yet passed the kind of rigorous, double-blind tests that we demand for determining the therapeutic value of a drug. I particularly

90

deplore fast-buck artists who are trying to sell do-it-yourself devices for controlling your brain waves at home. Therefore, I think that we should suspend judgment on the therapeutic effectiveness of alpha-wave training.

There are also these fantastic courses that some people are offering, that claim that you can get the ability for extrasensory perception and for diagnosing people at a distnace. This kind of thing uses the time-tested techniques of the fortune teller. All you need is some sort of line, like:

> *Your friends envy you. You seem so assured, in*
> *control of yourself and your life and you know*
> *what you are doing and where you are going. But*
> *if they only knew some of the thoughts that go*
> *on in your mind, or the kind of mask you are*
> *wearing to fool people. Why, they would be*
> *astonished that even the thought of suicide has*
> *flitted through your mind.*

If you talked to 10 people like that individually, you would get an electrifying reaction from nine, because such things go on in everyone's mind. These kind of tricks, I'm afraid, are being used by some people in this area.

What I would like to conclude with, then, is that I believe we have been too prejudiced against the autonomic nervous system and that western society, in general, has been unduly biased against the internal organs. We must carefully examine the proposition that we may be able with the aid of instrumentation to learn how to control visceral responses far more than we thought we could, and to correctly identify sensations from within us more accurately than we have thought we could. But we are still in the early experimental stages of this work and it's far too early to conclude what, if any, therapeutic applications will emerge from this new line of research.

I wish to acknowledge the support of the National Institutes of Health, Grants MH 13189 and MH 19183.

Biosynthesis and Metabolism of the Tobacco Alkaloids

By Edward Leete*

*Professor of Chemistry, the University of Minnesota

In the last 20 years a considerable amount of information has been obtained on the biosynthesis of the tobacco alkaloids, especially nicotine. Fig. 1 illustrates the various compounds which have been shown to be precursors of nicotine and their metabolic relationships. The enzymes responsible for carrying out some of these transformations have been isolated and purified. For example, a putrescine-N-methyltransferase was isolated from tobacco roots, and this enzyme catalyzed the formation of N-methylputrescine (III) from putrescine (IV) and S-adenosyl-L-methionine (1). An N-methylputrescine oxidase was also isolated (2) which catalyzed the formation of 4-methylaminobutanal (II). II cyclizes in acid media to the N-methyl-Δ^1-pyrrolinium salt (I)— the immediate precursor of the pyrrolidine ring of nicotine (3,4).

Dawson (5) established that the pyridine ring of nicotine is derived from nicotinic acid. This has been confirmed by others (6,7) who also showed that the point of attachment of the pyrrolidine ring of nicotine is at the site from which the carboxyl group is lost, *i.e.,* at C-3. However, the mechanism whereby nicotinic acid condenses with the N-methyl-Δ^1-pyrrolinium salt is still unknown. One experiment of Dawson which has been the subject of considerable discussion involved the use of nicotinic acid labeled around the pyridine ring with either tritium or deuterium. The isotopically labeled nicotinic acids were administered to sterile excised root cultures of *Nicotiana tabacum* for 4 weeks. The results of these experiments are recorded in Table I.

TABLE I

THE INCORPORATION OF NICOTINIC ACID INTO NICOTINE IN *N. tabacum*

Precursor fed	% Incorporation
[2-^{3}H]–Nicotinic acid	11.3
[4-^{2}H]–Nicotinic acid	13.0
[5-^{3}H]–Nicotinic acid	14.2
[6-^{3}H]–Nicotinic acid	1.1

The low incorporation of the [6–^{3}H]-nicotinic acid, compared with the other labeled acids required an explanation. We have now repeated the work of Dawson using intact tobacco plants, feeding [6–^{14}C, 2–^{3}H]- and [6–^{14}C, 6–^{3}H]-nicotinic acids to the plants by addition to the aqueous nutrient solution in which the roots were growing (8). The results of Dawson were confirmed, the nicotine derived from [6–^{14}C, 6–^{3}H]-nicotinic acid having lost 98% of its tritium relative to the carbon-14. On the other hand the nicotine derived from [6–^{14}C, 2–^{3}II]-nicotinic acid had essentially the same ^{3}H/^{14}C ratio as in the administered precursor. In order to determine whether the tritium was being lost from the [6–^{3}H]-nicotinic acid prior to its incorporation into nicotine, nicotinic acid was reisolated (by dilution with carrier nicotinic acid) from the plants harvested 8 days after the initial feeding. The reisolated nicotinic acid had the same ^{3}H/^{14}C ratio as in the administered [6–^{14}C, 6–^{3}H]-nicotinic acid, indicating that there was no loss of tritium by a reaction unrelated to nicotine biosynthesis, such as the formation of 6-hydroxynicotinic acid. We currently rationalize the loss of tritium from C-6 of nicotinic acid by the mechanism illustrated in Fig. 2. It is suggested that the nicotinic acid is reduced stereospecifically to yield 1,6-dihydronicotinic acid (V) which then condenses with the N-methyl-Δ^1-pyrrolinium salt to yield the intermediate VI. A concerted decarboxylation and loss of hydrogen at C-6 to a hydride acceptor (Z$^+$) then affords nicotine. Loss of tritium from the 6-position of the pyridine ring occurs if it is postulated that reactions (a) and (c) are both stereospecific, *i.e.,* the hydrogen introduced at C-6 on reduction of the nicotinic acid must have the opposite configuration from the hydrogen lost from this position in the final oxidative decarboxylation.

Even though we know very little about the detailed mech-

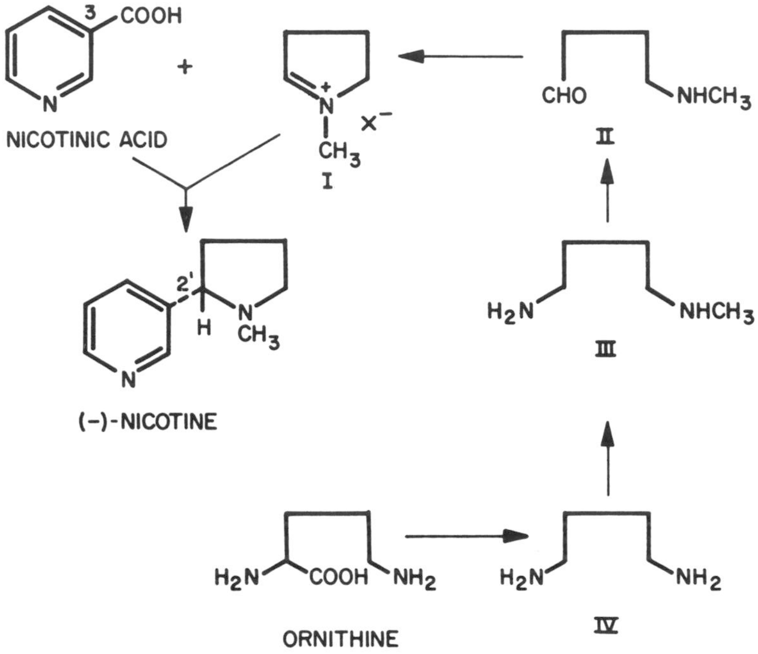

Fig. 1.   Biosynthetic precursors of nicotine.

anism of the condensation between nicotinic acid and the N-methyl-Δ^1-pyrrolinium salt, it has been discovered that the enzymatic reaction is not specific for these substrates. We found that the feeding of 5-fluoronicotinic acid (VII) to *N. tabacum* resulted in the formation of 5-fluoronicotine (VIII) (9). The 5-fluoronicotinic acid, in large doses, was phytotoxic to the plant. Thus, when a 3% aqueous solution of the fluoro compound was administered to the tobacco plant by the wick method, the stems became brown at the site of injection and the leaves near to the cotton wick became prematurely yellow and died after 2 to 3 days. A more dilute solution of 5-fluoronicotinic acid (<1%) was not toxic and no

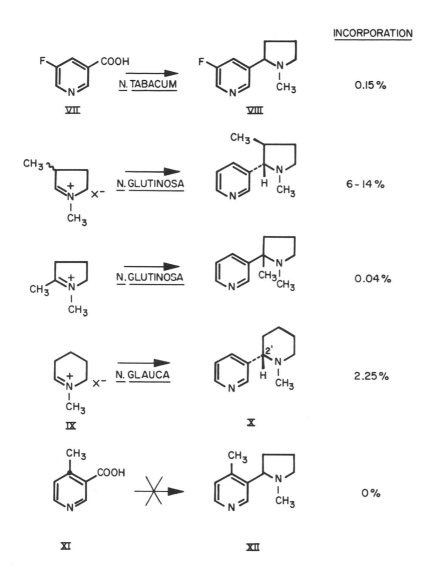

Fig. 2.   Hypothetic biosynthesis of nicotine.

obvious injury to the plant occurred. The tobacco plants were apparently able to build up some kind of resistance to the 5-fluoronicotinic acid. Thus, 4-month-old plants which had received 10 mg/day for 1 week were then able to tolerate increased amounts (up to 50 mg/day) with no ill effects. It was observed that non-lethal amounts of 5-fluoronicotinic acid inhibited the growth of tobacco when the compound was fed to the roots in hydroponics. New leaves were produced, but there was little stem elongation.

Rapoport (10) has found that methylated derivatives of the N-methyl-Δ^1-pyrrolinium salt are utilized by tobacco yielding methylated nicotines, as illustrated in Fig. 3. We have also found that the higher homologue of the pyrrolinium salt, namely N-methyl-Δ^1-piperideinium chloride (IX) yielded (−)-N-methylana-basine (X) in both N. tabacum and N. glauca (11). These homologues of nicotine had the same chirality at C-2′ as natural (−)-nicotine, strongly suggesting that the enzymes involved in nicotine biosynthesis were being utilized in these unnatural or aberrant reactions. Some of our attempts to produce unnatural nicotine analogues by this method have failed; thus, the administration of [4–^{14}C]-4-methylnicotinic acid (XI) to N. tabacum did not result in the formation of any 4-methylnicotine (XII). Possibly the large methyl group at C-4 sterically interfered with the condensation reaction.

In order to learn more about the modification of nicotinic acid required so that it will react with the N-methyl-Δ^1-pyrrolinium salt, we have examined the ability of simple 1,4-dihydropyridines to react with the pyrrolinium salt. Authentic 1,4-dihydropyridine (XIII) has been recently prepared (12). However, we considered that small amounts of XIII, or its tautomers would be present in an aqueous solution of glutaraldehyde and ammonia (13). Accordingly, glutaraldehyde, ammonia, and [2–^{14}C]-N-methylpyrrolinium acetate were mixed together at various pH's. After standing for 24 hours at room temperature, inactive nicotine was added to the mixture. The reisolated nicotine was purified by distillation and was crystallized to constant activity as its diperchlorate and dipicrate. Degradation indicated that all the activity of the nicotine was at C-2′ as expected. The radiochemical yields of nicotine obtained at various pH's are recorded in Table II.

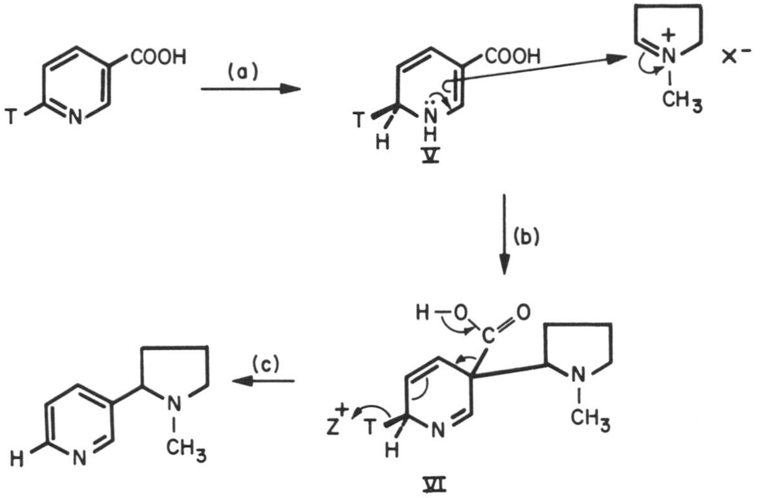

Fig. 3.   Some aberrant reactions in tobacco.

TABLE II

BIOMIMETIC SYNTHESIS OF NICOTINE FROM GLUTARALDEHYDE, AMMONIA, AND
N-METHYL-Δ^1-PYRROLINIUM ACETATE

pH of the reaction	Yield of nicotine (%)
3.3	1.8
4.9	5.8
5.6	8.0
6.1	10.8
8.9	17.4
10.3	21.2

Nicotine analogues could also be obtained by this reaction (14) as indicated in Fig. 4. Thus, glutaraldehyde, ammonia, and N-methyl-Δ^1-piperideinium chloride reacted together in the presence of air to yield N-methylanabasine (11.6% yield at pH 10.6). 3-Methyl-glutaraldehyde (XIV), ammonia, and the N-methyl-Δ^1-pyrrolinium salt yielded 4-methylnicotine, identical with an authentic sample prepared by an unambiguous method.

We have devised a new method for the synthesis of nicotine and its analogues (15) which is illustrated in Fig. 5. The key

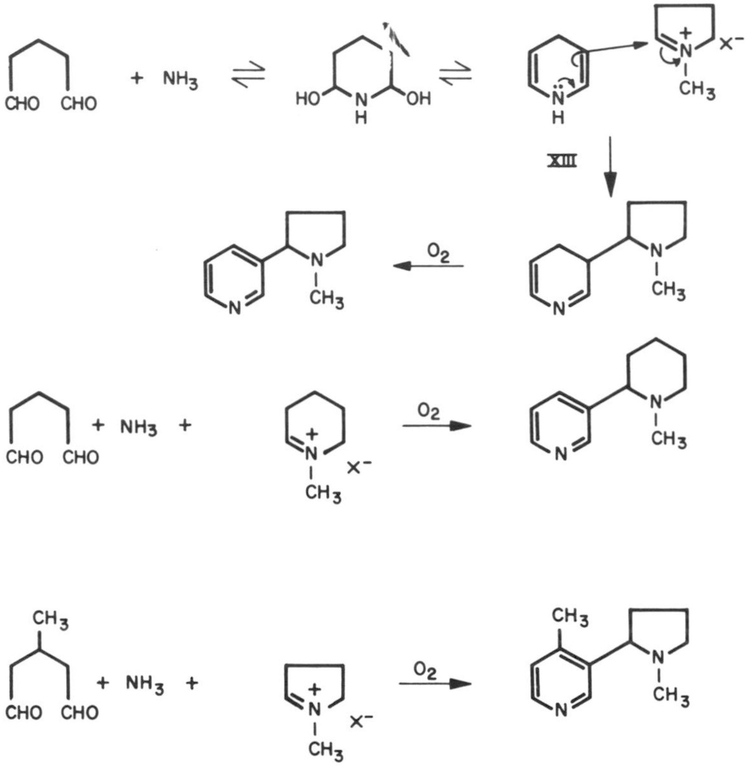

Fig. 4.   Biomimetic synthesis of nicotine, and analogues.

step in our synthesis of myosmine and nornicotine is the 1,4-addition of the carbanion of α-morpholino-α-(3-pyridyl)acetonitrile (XVI) to acrylonitrile, affording γ-cyano-γ-morpholino-γ-(3-pyridyl)butyronitrile (XVIII). Compound XVII was obtained by the addition of potassium cyanide to the iminium salt XV formed by heating pyridine-3-aldehyde with morpholine perchlorate in morpholine. Hydrolysis of XVIII with aqueous acetic acid yielded 3-cyano-1-(3-pyridyl)propan-1-one (XIX). Hydrogenation of this γ-ketonitrile in ethanolic ammonia in the presence of Raney nickel yielded the keto-amine (XX) which cyclized to myosmine. Nornicotine was obtained by reduction of the myosmine with sodium borohydride. Methylation with a mixture of formaldehyde and formic acid afforded nicotine.

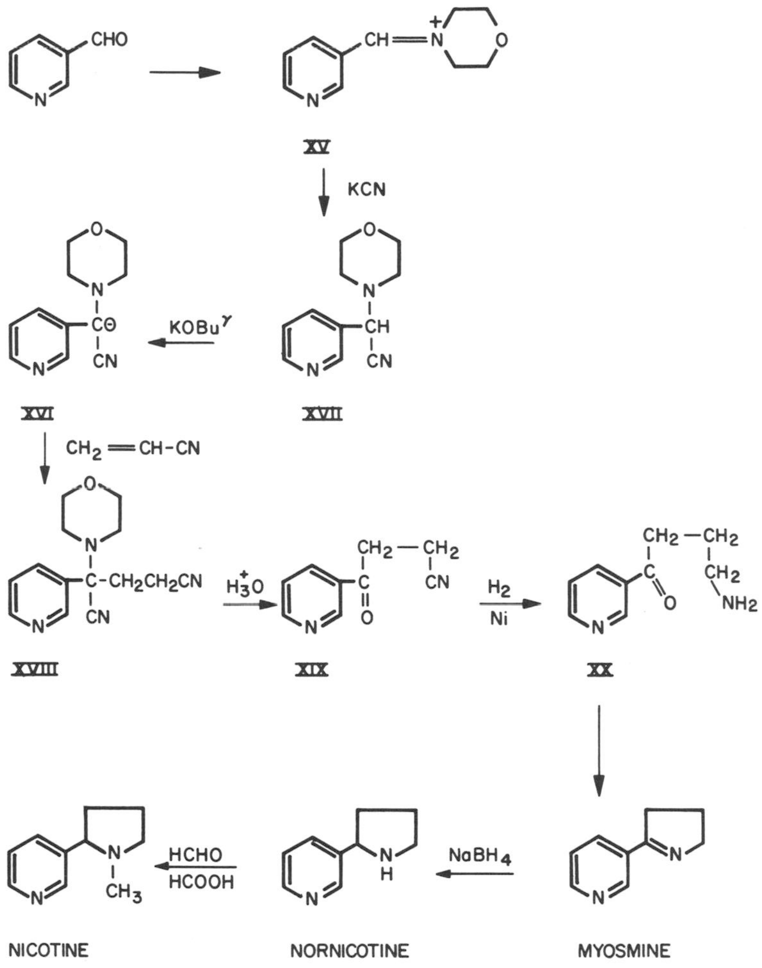

Fig. 5. Synthesis of nicotine, nornicotine, and myosmine.

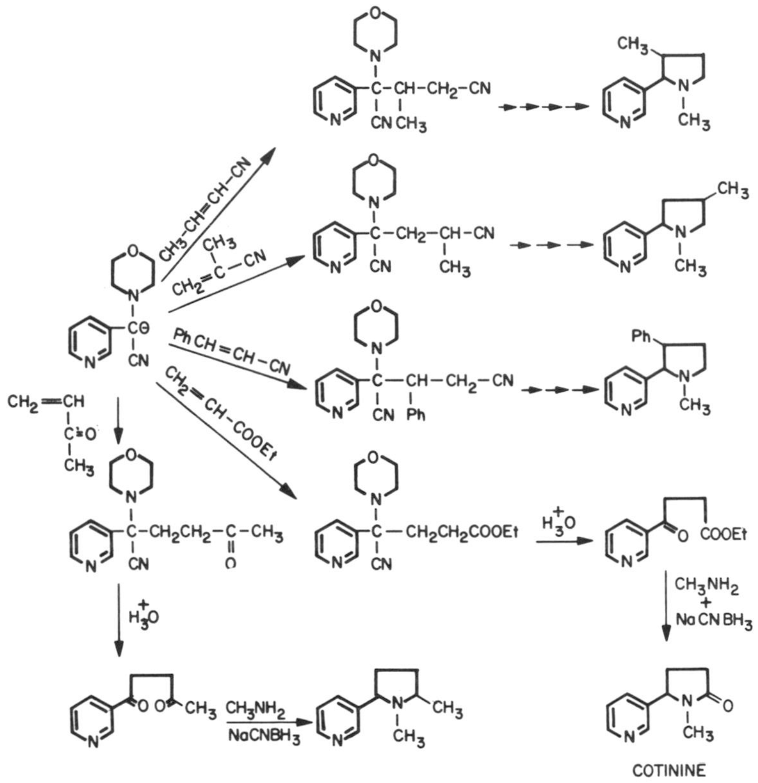

Fig. 6.　Synthesis of some nicotine analogues.

The synthesis of some nicotine analogues from the carbanion XVI are illustrated in Fig. 6. This carbanion was found to add to crotononitrile, α-methylacrylonitrile, cinnamoylnitrile, ethyl acrylate, methyl vinyl ketone, and acrolein. These addition products were then readily converted to nicotine derivatives as indicated. This synthesis was readily applicable to the preparation of isotopically labeled nicotine which was required for a study of nicotine metabolism in the healthy tobacco plant.

We do not regard nicotine as an end product of metabolism in the tobacco plant and we hoped to learn something about its function in the plant by studying its catabolism. We (16) and others (17) have shown that the N-methyl group of nicotine is readily lost by transmethylation. When [methyl–^{14}C]-nicotine was fed to *N. tabacum* radioactivity was detected in the N-methyl groups of choline. Recently we have fed [2'–^{14}C, 2'–^{3}H]-nicotine to *N. glauca* and searched for radioactive metabolites (18). Preliminary results are illustrated in Fig. 7. The percentage incorporation of carbon-14 activity into the various metabolites is indicated in brackets. A major pathway for the metabolism of nicotine in this species is apparently N-demethylation affording nornicotine. A dehydrogenation then yields myosmine, a component of tobacco smoke. Cotinine, a metabolite of nicotine in humans and other

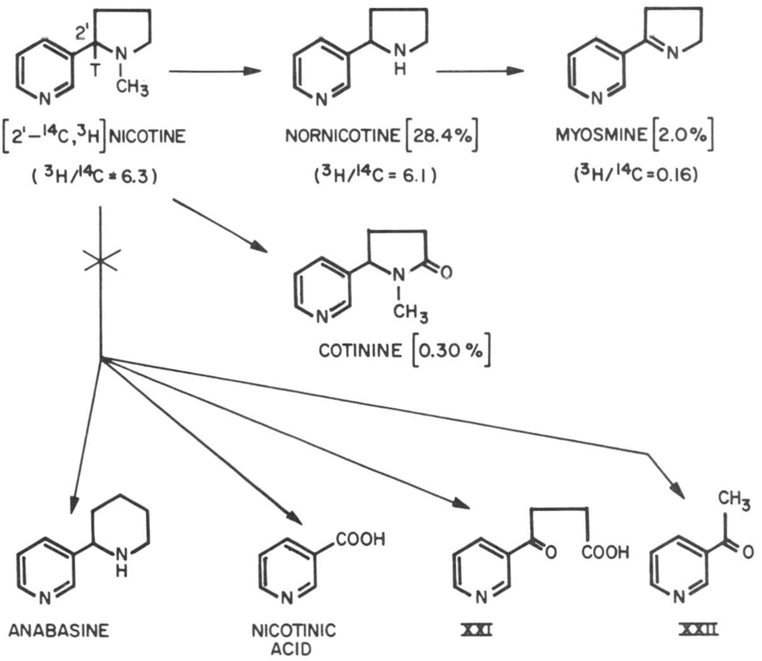

Fig. 7.   Metabolism of nicotine in *Nicotiana glauca* (for 3 days).

animals was also labeled. No activity was detected in anabasine. This confirmed our earlier observations (19), and hopefully put to rest the hypothesis (20) that anabasine can be formed from nicotine in tobacco. No activity was found in nicotinic acid, nicotinoylpropionic acid (XXI) or 3-acetylpyridine (XXII), which have been shown to be products from the microbial breakdown of nicotine.

In summary it can be said that there is much still to learn about the biochemistry of nicotine in the tobacco plant, but we are slowly gaining information on its biosynthesis and catabolism. In the future we will hopefully be able to say something about its biological role in this economically important plant.

In conclusion I acknowledge the enthusiastic contributions of my coworkers in these investigations on the tobacco alkaloids. They are as follows (with their current locations): Virginia M. Bell (retired from chemistry, Boston), Kenneth J. Siegfried (Quaker Oats Co., Chicago), Alan R. Friedman (Upjohn Co., Kalamazoo), Eduardo G. Gros (University of Buenos Aires, Argentina), Terry J. Gilbertson (Upjohn Co., Kalamazoo), Mary C. L. Louden (Lederle Co., Pearl River), Alan Fischer (University of North Dakota, Fargo), Edward E. Bellion (University of Texas, Arlington), C. Richard Hutchinson (University of Connecticut), Yu -Ying Liu (American Health Foundation, New York), Abdel Monheim Makky (University of Cairo, U.A.R.), Afzal Ahmad (Pakistan Institute of Nuclear Science, Rawalpindi), Henry V. Isaacson (Eastman Kodak, Rochester), H. Dupont Durst (SUNY at Buffalo), Marissa F. Manuel (retired from chemistry, Alberta), George B. Bodem, Miles R. Chedekel, Frank Hladek, Philip Hoekstra (graduate students at the University of Minnesota), and Fred Buchholtz (undergraduate at the University of Minnesota). The financial support of the National Institutes of Health, research grant GM-13246, is also gratefully acknowledged.

REFERENCES

1. S. Mizusaki, Y. Tanabe, M. Noguchi, and E. Tamaki, *Plant Cell Physiol.*, **12**, 633 (1971).
2. S. Mizusaki, Y. Tanabe, M. Noguchi, and E. Tamaki, *Phytochemistry*, **11**, 2757 (1972).

3. E. Leete, *J. Amer. Chem. Soc.*, **89**, 7081 (1967).
4. S. Mizusaki, T. Kisaki, and E. Tamaki, *Plant Physiol.*, **43**, 93 (1968).
5. R. F. Dawson, D. R. Christman, A. D'Adamo, M. L. Solt, and A. P. Wolf, *J. Amer. Chem. Soc.*, **82**, 2628 (1960).
6. K. S. Yang, R. K. Gholson, and G. R. Waller, *J. Amer. Chem. Soc.*, **87**, 4184 (1965).
7. T. A. Scott and J. P. Glynn, *Phytochemistry*, **6**, 505 (1967).
8. E. Leete and Yu-Ying Liu, *Phytochemistry*, **12**, 593 (1973) and unpublished work.
9. E. Leete, G. B. Bodem, and M. F. Manuel, *Phytochemistry*, **10**, 2687 (1971).
10. M. L. Rueppel and H. Rapoport, *J. Amer. Chem. Soc.*, **92**, 5528 (1970); *J. Amer. Chem. Soc.*, **93**, 7021 (1971).
11. E. Leete and M. R. Chedekel, *Phytochemistry*, **11**, 2751 (1972).
12. N. C. Cook and J. E. Lyons, *J. Amer. Chem. Soc.*, **88**, 3396 (1966); F. W. Fowler, *J. Org. Chem.*, **37**, 1321 (1972).
13. *c.f.* E. M. Kosower and T. S. Sorensen, *J. Org. Chem.*, **27**, 3764 (1962) who obtained 1,4-dihydropyridines by reaction of 3,3-dimethylglutaraldehyde with amines.
14. E. Leete, *J.C.S. Chem. Commun.*, 1091 (1972) and unpublished work.
15. E. Leete, M. R. Chedekel, and G. B. Bodem, *J. Org. Chem.*, **37**, 4465 (1972) and unpublished work with F. Buchholtz.
16. E. Leete and V. M. Bell, *J. Amer. Chem. Soc.*, **81**, 4358 (1959).
17. R. F. Dawson, *J. Amer. Chem. Soc.*, **73**, 4218 (1951).
18. E. Leete and M. R. Chedekel, unpublished work.
19. E. Leete, *Tetrahedron Letters*, 4433 (1968).
20. *c.f.* K. Mothes in "Biosynthesis of Aromatic Compounds," chapter 10, edited by G. Billek, Pergamon Press, 1966, p. 100.

Experimental Optimization of Column Efficiency in High-performance Liquid Chromatography

By J. J. KIRKLAND*

* Central Research Department
E.I. du Pont de Nemours & Company

Earlier in this symposium Lord Todd provided a good introduction to my topic, since he mentioned the need for special techniques to solve some of the difficult problems we now face in biochemistry, clinical and environmental chemistry.

The technique I will discuss—liquid chromatography (LC)— is a very old one; it was invented by Tswett, a Russian, at the turn of the century. After its inception the technique was employed in specialized areas but was not widely used. However, it received a particularly large boost from a 1941 paper on liquid-partition chromatography by A. J. P. Martin and Richard Synge (1). (Incidentally, Dr. Martin was a Philip Morris consultant for many years.) This paper—which resulted in a Nobel Prize for Martin and Synge—greatly stimulated interest in liquid chromatography. The paper also predicted gas chromatography (GC), and in 1952 Martin and A. T. James reported the first experiments on this new separations method (2). Gas chromatography has revolutionized separation science, and today a gas chromatograph is almost as common in the laboratory as a pH meter.

Partially as a result of the rapid development of gas chromatography as a fast and convenient high-resolution technique, the development of column liquid chromatography fell behind. But recently, there has been a strong revival in the interest and use of LC (3). This revival is due mainly to three reasons:

* *The LC process is now better understood, mostly as a result of theories derived from GC. Much GC information can be extra-*

polated into LC systems. The main difference lies in the moving phases for the two techniques.

* *New specialized equipment has been developed that makes LC more convenient and more precise. LC columns are now operated under high pressure using continuous, sensitive detectors which eliminate the tedium of collecting fractions to monitor the separations.*
* *More efficient columns have been developed, allowing separations to be carried out in minutes instead of hours or even days as was the case just a few years ago.*

Modern Liquid Chromatography

The tremendous strides taken in LC in recent years are illustrated in Fig. 1. In 1964 performance of LC columns was about 0.02 effective plates per second; this is representative of the performance of "classical" LC columns. Improvements in columns and equipment led to a decided increase in performance in about 1969. Hence, many take 1969 as a date of inception for so-called "modern liquid chromatography." It was at this time that specially designed packings to optimize column processes began to be available. Column performance improved as we better learned to utilize these special packings and the equipment was developed. More recently, the feasibility of making and using columns with very small particles ($<10\mu$) was demonstrated, and this again brought about a dramatic improvement in column performance (4,5).

Because LC columns can now be operated with high efficiency, separations of the kind shown in Fig. 2 are now possible. This is a separation of some hydroxylated aromatics by adsorption chromatography, the technique initially introduced by Tswett in 1902. The column used for the separation was only 25 cm long, but uses very small particles. The separation of these seven compounds required about a minute; more compounds actually could have been separated in the same time. The column was monitored with a very sensitive ultraviolet (UV) photometric detector.

It should be noted that with such small particles, columns have poor permeability. Therefore, the "price" for rapid LC separations is the high pressure which is needed to force the mobile phase through the column bed.

Since we have gas chromatography and thin-layer chromatography (TLC) as powerful separation methods, why is there a need for liquid chromatography? GC, although obviously an excellent high-resolution technique, is limited in that only about 20% of our known compounds are sufficiently volatile for analysis. On the other hand, LC can be used for non-volatile compounds, as well as ionic species and compounds of poor thermal stability. TLC, which involves an open chromatographic bed, also is widely used for these types of compounds. In many ways TLC complements column chromatography quite nicely.

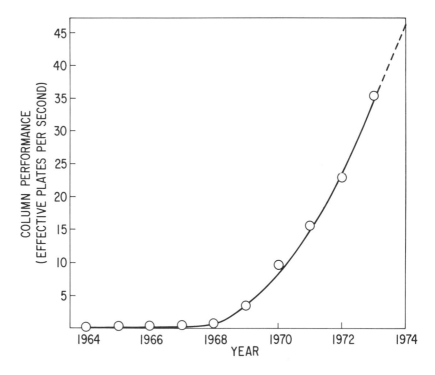

Fig. 1. Column performance measured as effective plates per second as a function of year.

HIGH-SPEED SEPARATION of HYDROXYLATED AROMATICS

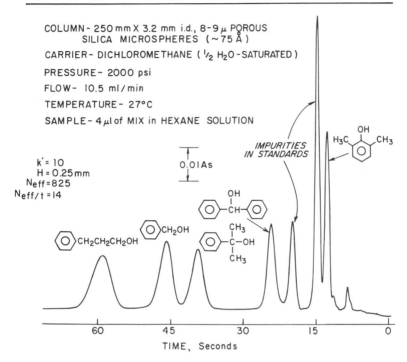

Fig. 2.   A high-performance liquid chromatogram.

But column chromatography has certain advantages over TLC. One is the capability for precise quantitation. In our laboratory we have assay methods which routinely determine the main component to 0.5% relative or better (6). Another advantage of LC is the ability to generate a large number of theoretical plates to carry out difficult separations promptly. Thirdly, we can isolate pure compounds. Lately, some workers have been preparing fractions of grams—even grams—of highly pure material using high-performance columns up to one inch in diameter.

Therefore, column liquid chromatography functions uniquely in certain situations. In our analytical facilities we try to take an integrated approach to separation science, using whatever separation technique appears best for a given problem.

What is different about *modern* liquid chromatography? The chemistry of the separation process has not changed—it is the same as it has been since 1902. Therefore, all the literature is quite relevant to current problems. What *has* changed is the physics of the separation process. Flow dynamics has been optimized, so that LC separations may be carried out 100 to 1000 times faster than was possible only eight or 10 years ago. Mixtures can be separated 10 to 100 times faster than with the best TLC procedures.

In this paper I would like to discuss briefly how column efficiency in modern LC is experimentally optimized. It should be noted that we are in a relatively early period in the development of high-performance LC, probably corresponding to about 1957 in the history of GC. Therefore, we can anticipate sizable improvements in resolution and convenience.

Some Simple Chromatographic Theory

We need to have simple relationships before attempting a discussion of column performance. Fig. 3 is a typical liquid chromatogram. A sample is injected into a column and is developed with mobile phase, using a high-pressure pump to carefully control the flow. The solvent front and any unretained solutes in the chromatogram elute in time t_0. In this illustration two compounds are separated to which we assign retention times t_{R1} and t_{R2}. Under constant separating conditions these retention times characterize the compounds in question. These compounds separate in the form of bands with widths W_1 and W_2. The narrower the bands or peaks, the higher the efficiency of the column and the better the separation. The resolution of these two compounds is characterized by the expression:

$$R_S = \frac{(t_{R2} - t_{R1})}{\frac{1}{2}(W_1 + W_2)} \qquad \text{(Eq. 1)}$$

which tells how well the separation is conducted. R_S is a number value for the degree of separation that we obtain in a particular chromatographic run.

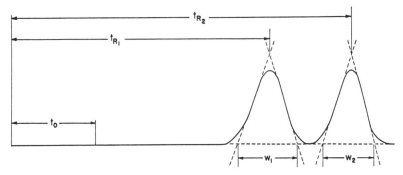

Fig. 3.   Model liquid chromatographic separation
in terms of retention times and peak width.

Equation 1 is a very useful expression from a simplistic viewpoint, but unfortunately it does not indicate what has to be done experimentally to improve resolution. However, there is another equation which can be derived which predicts specific ways to optimize R_S. To a first approximation the equation is:

$$R_S = \tfrac{1}{4}(\alpha - 1) \left(\frac{k'}{1 + k'}\right) (N^{1/2}) \qquad \text{(Eq. 2)}$$

where

$$k' = \frac{t_R - t_0}{t_0} \, ,$$

$$\alpha = \frac{k_2'}{k_1'} \, ,$$

and

$$N = 16 \left(\frac{t_R}{W}\right)^2$$

In equation 2 the term $(\alpha - 1)$ is a *separation factor*, $k'/(1 + k')$

is a *capacity factor,* and $N^{1/2}$ is the *plate number* for the column. The parameters represented by these three terms control the resolution of the chromatographic separation and these parameters can be experimentally optimized separately.

The capacity factor, k', is defined as the total moles of solute in the stationary phase divided by the total moles of solute in the mobile phase. If the solute is completely unretained by the column, then $k' = 0$. The capacity factor is controlled by changing the strength of the mobile phase. If the peak is too far out in the chromatogram (*i.e.,* solute too strongly retained), the strength of the mobile phase should be increased. If the solute peak is too close to the solvent front, the strength of the mobile phase should be decreased. Under optimum conditions, k' should be adjusted to have a value between one and 10.

The value α is the ratio of the capacity factors for the two peaks in a given chromatogram. Both the separation factor α and the capacity factor k' involve thermodynamic functions. As suggested in equation 2, α should be made as large as possible. While there are some guidelines for manipulating α, a trial-and-error process is normally used for optimizing this separation variable.

N represents the theoretical plate count for the chromatographic column. It relates to the sharpness of the peaks and indicates how well the column has been prepared. Another function, H, is defined in terms of N as:

$$H = \frac{L}{N}$$
(Eq. 3)

where L = column length.

H is sometimes referred to as HETP (*i.e.,* height equivalent to a theoretical plate). In the preparation of chromatographic columns a large value of N (small H) is sought for good resolution. Early in the development of chromatographic theory, H was thought to be the theoretical distance a solute molecule had to move before engaging in a chromatographic interaction. This is an over-simplified picture. However, the H value is useful as a concept to guide in the construction of efficient columns. By minimizing band broadening we minimize H and improve chromatographic resolution.

What can we do to effect a complete separation of two incompletely resolved peaks? The approaches are represented by the chromatograms in Fig. 4. By varying k', we can either force compounds through the column faster (resulting in poor resolution) or retain them longer (giving a better separation). However, as k' approaches a value of 10, there is little further improvement in resolution as k' is increased. Furthermore, at this point the peaks start to broaden considerably, because the solutes are in the column longer. A k' value between two and five represents the best compromise to obtain maximum resolution in minimum time. Values in this range are obtained by properly adjusting the

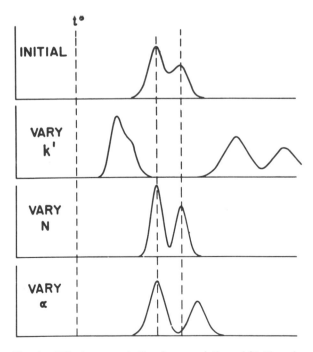

Fig. 4.   Effects on resolution from variation of k', N, and α.

strength of the mobile phase. If solvents permitting different selectivity are tested to effect a desired separation, the value of k' should still be maintained in this range.

Another means of improving resolution is to increase N, the column plate number. By optimizing the particles and the packing process, we can construct a better column and increase N. We also can increase N by increasing the length of the column. Of course, as the length of the column increases, so does the pressure required to maintain the flow of mobile phase.

Alternatively, resolution can be improved by making α as large as possible by changing one of the phases involved in the chromatographic process. In most liquid chromatographic systems it is more convenient to change the mobile phase to increase α. There are some guidelines to help in the selection of mobile phases to maximize α (3a, 3d).

Band Broadening—the Physical Process

The total plate height, H_T, represents the extent that a band has broadened during the chromatographic run. This function can be expressed as the sum of five terms, each of which corresponds to a physical phenomenon in the chromatographic process:

$$H_T = H_E + H_M + H_S + H_{SM} + H_{EC} \qquad \text{(Eq. 4)}$$

In this equation H_E is the plate height due to multiple flow paths (so-called "eddy diffusion" term) within the chromatographic column. H_M is the plate height due to resistance to mobile-phase mass transfer (*i.e.*, the extent of non-equilibrium in the mobile-phase processes). H_S is defined as a plate height due to limitations in stationary-phase mass transfer, and H_{SM} is the plate height due to stagnant-mobile-phase mass-transfer effects. H_{EC} is a plate height resulting from extra-column band-broadening effects. Fig. 5 schematically shows how four of these processes contribute to band broadening during flow through a packed chromatographic bed. Each of these processes will now be considered separately.

Eddy Diffusion. Some of the channels in this packed bed are smaller than others. This condition causes a gradation of flow, so that after a given time some molecules have traveled further down

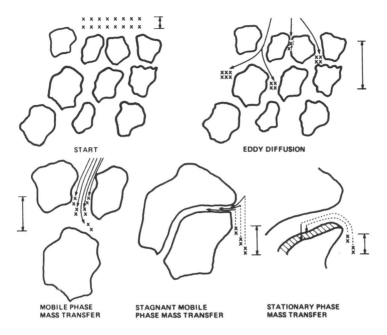

Fig. 5.   Effects of various band-broadening factors in a flowing system.

the column than others. By the time the solute molecule has eluted, the band has broadened considerably as a result of this effect.

Mobile-phase Limitations. The flow of mobile phase through a channel between particles also shows a velocity gradient. Solute molecules which come in close contact with the surface—either the column wall or the surface of a stationary particle—move at a different rate than solute molecules in the middle of the flow stream. The result of this solute velocity gradient is band broadening.

Stagnant-mobile-phase Limitations. Solute molecules moving down the column have access to pores within particles in the packed bed. Sample molecules which diffuse deeply into the pores are left somewhat behind in the flow-stream, because it takes a relatively long time for them to re-emerge into the flow pattern.

(Remember that diffusion is slow in liquids.) This process is a significant band-spreading mechanism in LC.

Stationary-phase Mass Transfer. Solute molecules can penetrate into a stationary film (*e.g.,* ion exchanger or stationary liquid) on the surface of the solid support to varying degrees. Once again, a solute velocity gradient is obtained, because solute molecules which penetrate the film more deeply require a longer time to re-emerge into the flow pattern than do molecules which do not interact as extensively.

Extra-column Effects. Significant band broadening can occur as a result of "dead volumes," in the apparatus outside the column, which are poorly swept by the mobile phase. Some aspects of this problem are discussed below.

Band Broadening—How to Minimize It

What can we do experimentally to minimize all of these band-broadening effects?

Eddy Diffusion. To reduce band broadening due to eddy diffusion we attempt to build a very homogeneous packing structure within the column bed. As shown in Fig. 6, one way is to use spherical particles in the column. The spherical particles on the left generally form a more organized, tightly knit structure than do irregularly shaped particles on the right. Hence, the average dimension of the channels in the column bed is smaller in the case of spheres than for randomly shaped particles. The closer together the particles, the more quickly the solute molecules can achieve the desired chromatographic interaction.

Another way to reduce unwanted eddy diffusion is to use packing particles that have a narrow size range (4). Fig. 7 illustrates some new particles especially made for high-performance LC. These particles are all about the same size: five to six μ $\pm$ 20%. Use of closely sized particles makes it easier to achieve a uniform packing structure, particularly with particles of $<10\mu$.

A third method for reducing eddy-diffusional effects is to optimize the packing process. The best column-packing method depends on the type and size of particles. Very small particles (*e.g.,* $<20\mu$) should be packed by a wet-packing method (5,7).

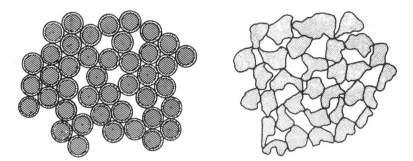

Fig. 6. Minimizing eddy diffusion through the use of particles with spherical, rather than irregular, shapes.

Fig. 7. Minimizing band broadening with particles having a narrow size range. From *J. Chromatog. Sci.*, **10,** 593 (1972). © 1972 by Preston Technical Abstracts Company. Reprinted by permission.

However, if the particles are larger than about 20μ, they can be dry-packed (8). Fig. 8 shows that the uniform dry-packing of $30\text{-}\mu$ particles by a machine reduces the plate height by about 50%, compared to the dry-packing of the same particles by hand. Also, much smaller spread of H values is obtained using the machine dry-packing process. Many commercial suppliers now use machines to pack columns so that this particular band-broadening effect can be minimized.

Recently, another approach to reducing band broadening as a result of unwanted flow effects has evolved. This approach has not been used generally, but it does have some special applications which will be mentioned later. In packing (especially dry-packing) columns, the greatest non-uniformity occurs near the column walls. Consequently, the column bed is more permeable around the area of the wall, and the velocity of the mobile phase is higher in this region. As shown in Fig. 9a and 9b, the velocity gradient across narrow-bore columns as a result of this higher flow near the wall is averaged out by a trans-column equilibration. This is the result of the radial dispersion of the solute molecules across the column cross-section. This trans-column equilibration can take place several times during the passage of the solute molecules down the column. However in unfavorable situations the solute molecules reach the more permeable area around the column walls, but never get a chance to achieve this smoothing-out process (Fig. 9c). This situation can cause badly broadened peaks—even doublet peaks. However, by selecting the proper particle size, column internal diameter, and column length, an "infinite-diameter" column effect can be achieved (9). In this case sample molecules that are carefully introduced into the top center of the column never reach the heterogeneous portion of the column near the walls. As a result, only the uniform center of the column is used in the separating process (Fig. 9d). Infinite-diameter columns have given the best separations of any yet reported for high-performance liquid chromatography.

The photographs in Fig. 10 show that an unretained solute peak travels coherently through an "infinite-diameter" column. The column is a 1 1/4-inch-diameter bed of silica gel with a mobile phase to match the refractive index of the packing, so that a dye

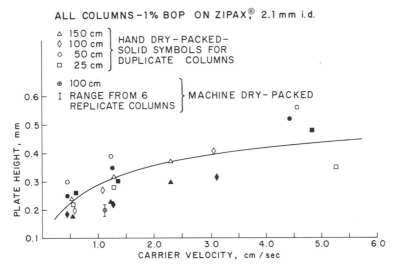

Fig. 8.   Plate height vs. velocity curves for hand-dry-packed columns compared to machine-dry-packed columns.

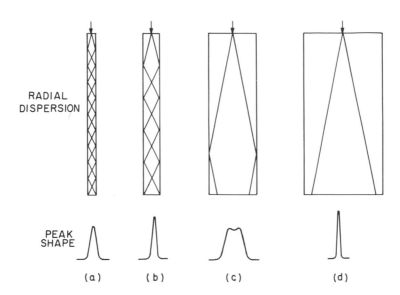

Fig. 9.   The effect of radial dispersion on peak shape effects in "infinite-diameter" column.

Fig. 10. Photograph of a dyestuff flowing through an "infinite-diameter" column. As the peaks flow through, very little band broadening occurs. (Courtesy of J. J. DeStefano.)

compound is visible as it moves down the column. The photographs taken of the solute band show that the initial band size increases very little as it passes through the column. Note that none of the solute approaches the column walls. Columns operating in this so-called "infinite-diameter" mode produce chromatographic peaks which are quite sharp, as indicated at the bottom of Fig. 9d.

Mobile-phase Limitations. Generally, band broadening resulting from resistance to mass transfer in the mobile phase can be reduced by using columns of small-diameter particles. Mass transfer is faster and more efficient in a bed of small particles, as the schematic in Fig. 11 illustrates. How small should these particles be? There are practical limitations, of course. It is difficult to pack a homogeneous bed of five-μ particles in a routine fashion, and special techniques have been developed for preparing very high-

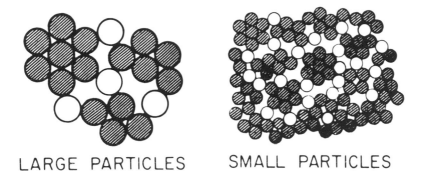

LARGE PARTICLES   SMALL PARTICLES

Fig. 11. Packings of large and small particles.

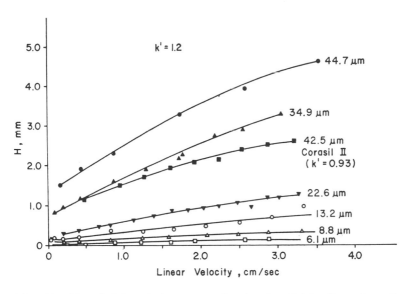

Fig. 12. Plate height-velocity curves showing beneficial effect of small particle sizes on plate heights. From *J. Chromatog. Sci.,* **11,** 88 (1973). © 1973 by Preston Technical Abstracts Company. Reprinted by permission.

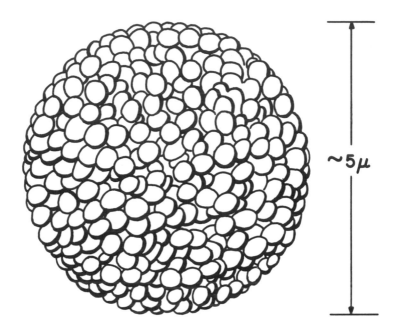

~5μ

Fig. 13. Porous silica microspheres; above, schematic and right, electron-micrograph. From *J. Chromatog. Sci.*, **10**, 593 (1972). © 1972 by Preston Technical Abstracts Company. Reprinted by permission.

efficiency beds of these materials (5,7). The family of performance curves in Fig. 12 illustrates that the highest column efficiencies (*i.e.*, smallest plate heights) are achieved with the smallest particles. The materials used in this case were wide-pore silica gels, with sizes ranging from 45 down to six μ (10).

In our laboratories we have been working with very small, totally porous silica microspheres (4,11,12). These microspheres (Fig. 13) are made by the agglutination of very small colloidal particles of silica (13). The pores within the microspheres result from spaces left between these very small particles. The silica microspheres can be made with varying porosities and sizes for

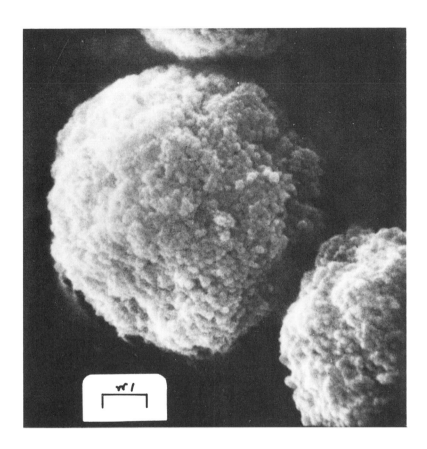

carrying out any of the modern LC methods: adsorption, liquid-partition, and exclusion chromatography. For example, high-surface-area microspheres (250 m^2/g) of eight-to-nine-μ particles have been used to obtain the separation of some substituted urea herbicides by adsorption chromatography in about six minutes, as shown in Fig. 14.

Stationary-phase Effects. In many forms of modern liquid chromatography, stationary-phase effects are not a dominant factor in peak broadening. For example, see Fig. 15. A liquid-liquid chromatographic column with one-% liquid phase (β,β'-oxydi-propionitrile) shows identical efficiency as the same packing with a three-% liquid-phase loading. However stationary-phase effects can become important in use of ion exchangers and chemically bonded stationary phases. Mass transfer in these polymeric, high-viscosity media is slow. This problem can be minimized by using very thin films of these polymer phases on the packing support.

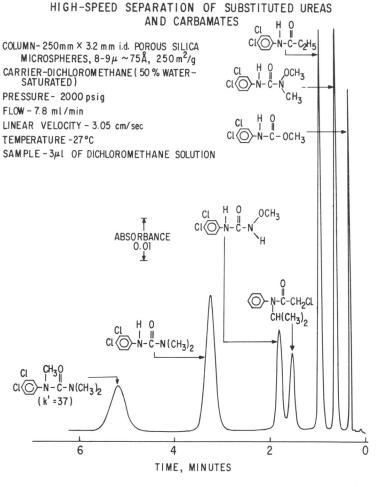

Fig. 14. Separation of some substituted-urea herbicides using porous silica microspheres. From "Gas Chromatography 1972." © 1973 by Applied Science Publishers, Ltd. Reprinted by permission.

Stagnant-mobile-phase Effects. These effects can be a major cause of band broadening in LC and special care must be taken to minimize this problem. Consider a totally porous 30-μ particle of silica gel such as that shown at the right of Fig. 16. Being totally porous, relatively deep pools of stagnant mobile phases are formed within these particles. The time required for solute molecules to move in and out of these deep pools is relatively long. Thus, the mass-transfer process can be dominated by the slow equilibrium involved.

To minimize these effects very small particles are employed. The other solution is to use particles which have a solid core and

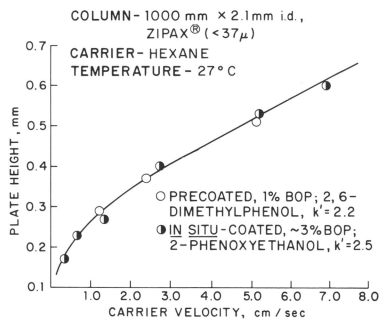

Fig. 15. Effect of varying stationary phase concentration on the plate height-carrier velocity curve. The stationary liquid used was β,β'-oxydipropionitrile. From *Anal. Chem.*, **45,** 1778 (1973). © 1973 by the American Chemical Society. Reprinted by permission.

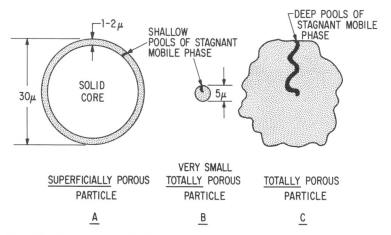

Fig. 16. Stagnant-mobile-phase effects can be minimized through (a) use of solid-core particles with thin, porous shells and (b) use of very small particles.

a very thin porous shell. Fig. 17 shows a schematic and cross-section electronmicrograph of one of these so-called superficially porous (porous-layer bead) packings (15). The porous surface of this Zipax[R] [in this manuscript superscript [R] refers to a registered trademark of a product of E.I. du Pont de Nemours & Company] controlled-surface-porosity particle is made up of layers of 200-mμ balls of silica (the solid core appears at the bottom of the figure). In this particular particle the pores are about 1000 Å and the porous shell is one or two μ thick. The chromatographic sorbent is deposited as a thin accessible film in the porous shell. Fig. 18 shows a chromatogram of a test mixture of hydroxylated aromatics which was obtained in about 75 seconds utilizing a packing of Zipax[R] to minimize the stagnant-mobile-phase effects. Particles of the superficially porous or porous-layer bead type are now available from several manufacturers (16,17). Columns of these materials are useful not only for precise quantitative measurements but also can be utilized for trace analysis—for example, pesticides (18).

Extra-column Effects. Poorly swept pockets of mobile phase in the injection or detector systems (*i.e.,* "dead volumes") can cause significant extra-column band broadening. Equipment must be constructed properly to minimize such effects. The data in Table I indicate the increase in plate heights that can occur with a very high-efficiency column as a function of the volume of the detector cell.

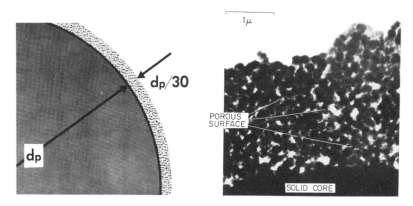

Fig. 17. Zipax[R]—a type of superficially porous material—left, schematic and right, cross-section electronmicrograph. From *J. Chromatog. Sci.,* **7,** 361 (1969). © 1969 by Preston Technical Abstracts Company. Reprinted by permission.

With $k' \leq$ two, there is significant increase in plate heights measured with an eight-μl cell (common in commercially available UV photometric detectors) as compared to a specially designed one-μl cell. Therefore, large cell volumes can significantly broaden peaks that move through the column quickly. Some peaks of interest are only about 50 μl in volume; these require very small detector volumes to prevent extra-column band broadening.

Appreciable band spreading can also occur during injection of the sample. Again, this is a particular problem with very high-efficiency systems, as illustrated in Table II. In this study the samples were introduced into a very high-efficiency column using different injection techniques. The best method was a direct in-

TABLE I
EFFECT OF DETECTOR CELL VOLUME (11)

Cell volume	Run no.	Solute Plate Heights (cm)[a]				
		2,6-Dimethyl-phenol ($k' = 0.53$)	Benzhydrol ($k' = 2.2$)	α,α-Dimethyl-benzyl alcohol ($k' = 4.3$)	Benzyl alcohol ($k' = 5.2$)	3-Phenyl-1-propanol ($k' = 7.1$)
1 μl	1	0.0119	0.0092	0.0094	0.0084	0.0079
	2	0.0111	0.0088	0.0087	0.0079	0.0075
	3	0.0124	0.0108	0.0094	0.0082	0.0073
	4	0.0115	0.0103	0.0082	0.0081	0.0072
Average		0.0117	0.0098	0.0089	0.0081	0.0075
Std. dev.		0.0005	0.0009	0.0006	0.0002	0.0003
8 μl	1	0.0116	0.0167	0.0090	0.0094	0.0081
	2	0.0140	0.0180	0.0111	0.0097	0.0074
	3	0.0146	0.0125	0.0097	0.0087	0.0078
	4	0.0131	0.0120	0.0093	0.0082	0.0075
Average		0.0133	0.0148	0.0098	0.0090	0.0077
Std. dev.		0.0013	0.0030	0.0008	0.0007	0.0003

[a] Column parameters: 250 mm $\times$ 3.2 mm id, 8–9 μ porous silica microspheres, 250 m^2/g; carrier, dichloromethane (50% water-saturated); carrier flow rate, 1.97 ml/minute; carrier velocity, 0.65 cm/second; pressure 510 psig; sample, 4 μl of 2.4 mg/ml each in dichloromethane, except 1.0 mg/ml benzhydrol; temperature, 27°C.

jection into the top of the packing with a microsyringe (so-called "on-column" technique). However, this often is not a practical procedure since this approach disturbs the packing and eventually degrades column performance. Therefore, various types of plugs were placed in the inlet of the columns (*e.g.,* porous plugs made from Teflon[R] TFE fluorocarbon resins, etc.) and samples injected onto these plugs. Also tested were different types of needles used with the microsyringe. All of these measures invariably increased plate height and broadened the peak of the test compounds.

It was determined that by placing a thin, porous metal screen on top of the column bed, results could be obtained that compared favorably with those of the on-column technique. Small-volume, specially designed valves can also be used to produce separations

HIGH SPEED SEPARATION WITH MACHINE PACKED COLUMN

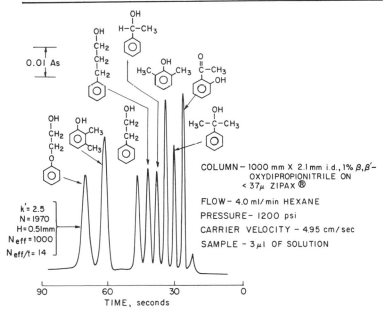

COLUMN – 1000 mm X 2.1 mm i.d., 1% β,β'-
OXYDIPROPIONITRILE ON
< 37μ ZIPAX ®

FLOW – 4.0 ml/min HEXANE

PRESSURE – 1200 psi

CARRIER VELOCITY – 4.95 cm/sec

SAMPLE – 3 μl OF SOLUTION

$k' = 2.5$
$N = 1970$
$H = 0.5$ mm
$N_{eff} = 1000$
$N_{eff}/t = 14$

Fig. 18.   Separation of a test mixture of phenols using Zipax[R], a commercially available superficially porous material.

TABLE II
EFFECT OF SAMPLING CONDITIONS (11)

Inlet Sampling Conditions	Column #1			Column #2		
	No. runs	k'	Plate height	No. runs	k'	Plate height
A	3	2^b	0.0097 ±0.0014	2	2	0.0121 ±0.0003
	3	6^c	0.0097 ±0.0005	2	6	0.0097 ±0.0001
B	1	2	0.0307			
	1	6	0.0222			
C	1	2	0.0163			
	1	6	0.0151			
D	4	2	0.0161 ±0.0021	2	2	0.0189 ±0.0007
	4	6	0.0171 ±0.0022	2	6	0.0156 ±0.0011
E	2	2	0.0155 ±0.0003	5	2	0.0197 ±0.0018
	2	6	0.0163 ±0.0004	5	6	0.0149 ±0.0025
F						
G						

with equivalent efficiency. These studies show that sample inlet systems must be carefully designed to maintain the integrity of high-efficiency LC columns.

Summary. By observing the precautions named above, significant improvements in the performance of the LC columns can be obtained. Fig. 19 presents plate height versus mobile-phase velocity curves for columns of various commercially available packings. The steep plot for data from diatomaceous-earth packing reflects significant band broadening from stagnant-mobile-phase effects, and also the relatively large particle size of this packing. The porous-layer-bead packings result in less steep plots, *i.e.,* increasing the mobile-phase velocity does not greatly increase plate height, particularly with Zipax[R]. (This is why high pressure is required in modern LC—high mobile-phase velocities can be used

	Plate Heights (cm)[a]							
Column #3			Column #4			Column #5		
No. runs	k'	Plate height	No. runs	k'	Plate height	No. runs	k'	Plate height
2	2	0.0281 ±0.0002						
2	6	0.0143 ±0.0001						
4	2	0.0201 ±0.0066						
4	6	0.0138 ±0.0016						
			5	2	0.0096 ±0.0004	3	2	0.0107 ±0.0005
			5	6	0.0083 ±0.0006	3	6	0.0086 ±0.0002
						4	2	0.0109 ±0.0023
						4	6	0.0075 ±0.0012

[a] Conditions same as in Table I.

[b] Benzhydrol; actual values, 1.8—2.1.

[c] 3-Phenyl-1-propanol; actual values, 6.3—7.1

Quoted tolerances are maximum spread of values (approximately 3 delta).

Key to Inlet Sampling Conditions:

A—On column injection, pointed needle into packing, *ca.* 5 mm.

B—Porous TFE plug, ⅛-inch thick, 10μ; pointed needle.

C—Same as B, except square-tipped needle.

D—Porous stainless steel plug, ⅛-inch thick, 10μ; pointed needle.

E—Same as D, except square-tipped needle.

F—Stainless steel screen 0.0006-inch thick, 5μ; pointed needle.

G—Same as F, except modified Hamilton valve.

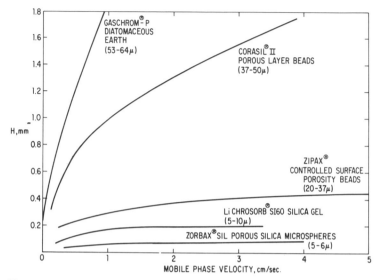

Fig. 19. A summary of plate height vs. carrier velocity curves for some commercially available LC packings.

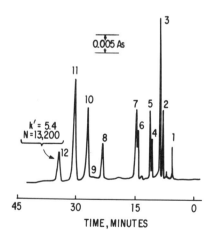

Fig. 20. A chromatogram obtained under optimum conditions for very high resolution. Using a series of four 25-cm columns containing five-μ particles, a total of 13,200 effective plates was obtained for separation of a test mixture of substituted phenols. From *J. Chromatog.*, **83,** 149 (1973). © 1973 by Elsevier Scientific Publishing Company. Reprinted by permission.

with small particles without significant decrease in column performance.) The flattest plate height versus velocity curves, as well as the lowest plate heights, are obtained with columns of very small particles.

Separation Efficiency—the Upper Limit

A comparison of column efficiencies in chromatography is presented in Table III. Classical packed gas chromatography columns can achieve about 10 effective plates/second. Open capillary GC columns (so-called open-tubular columns) will provide up to about 25 plates/second; packed capillaries yield about 40.

TABLE III
COMPARISON OF COLUMN EFFICIENCIES IN CHROMATOGRAPHY

Technique	Column Type	dp or dc (μ)	Max. N_{eff}/second
GC	Classical packed	130	10
GC	Open tubular	250	25
GC	Packed capillary	10	40
LC	Classical packed	150	0.02
LC	Silica gel closely sized	20	2
LC	Porous-layer bead (Zipax[R])	27	10
LC	Porous-layer bead "infinite diameter"	27	16
	Silica gel, high performance	5–10	15
	Porous microspheres	5–6	37

Prior to about 1964 a classical packed column in LC would exhibit about 0.02 effective plates/second. However, column performance has since dramatically improved and is now at a level of more than 35 effective plates/second. Theory suggests that we can anticipate a practical upper limit of about 100 effective plates/second for optimum LC systems.

Lord Todd previously mentioned that we need high performance systems for mixtures that are difficult to separate. This raises a question: Can LC columns be sequenced—cascaded in series—to obtain a very high degree of separation, *i.e.*, very high resolution? The answer is yes. Fig. 20 is a chromatogram which was obtained on a series of four 25-cm columns made from five-μ adsorbant particles. For this particular separation of substituted phenolic compounds, more than 13,200 effective plates were exhibited by this column. It is apparent that we can successfully connect columns in series, provided that extra-column band-broadening phenomena are effectively controlled.

Conclusions

High-performance column liquid chromatography is now a major analytical tool. It has found wide acceptance in many laboratories, taking its rightful place with gas chromatography and thin-layer chromatography as a high-resolution technique. As a result of theoretical insight the traditional art of column liquid chromatography (some have called it witchcraft) has now evolved into a modern, scientifically based method.

REFERENCES

1. A. J. P. Martin and R. L. M. Synge, *Biochem. J.*, **35**, 1358 (1941).
2. (a) A. T. James and A. J. P. Martin, *Biochem. J.*, **50**, 679 (1952); (b) A. T. James and A. J. P. Martin, *The Analyst*, **77**, 915 (1952).
3. (a) "Modern Practice of Liquid Chromatography," J. J. Kirkland, editor, Wiley Interscience, New York, 1971; (b) N. Hadden *et al.*, "Basic Liquid Chromatography," Varian Aerograph, Walnut Creek, California, 1972; (c) S. G. Perry, R. Amos, and P. I. Brewer, "Practical Liquid Chromatography," Plenum Press, New York, 1972; (d) L. R. Snyder and J. J. Kirkland, "Introduction to Modern Liquid Chromatography," Wiley Interscience, New York, 1974.
4. J. J. Kirkland, *J. Chromatog. Sci.*, **10**, 593 (1972).
5. R. E. Majors, *Anal. Chem.*, **44**, 1722 (1972).
6. R. E. Leitch, *J. Chromatog. Sci.*, **9**, 531 (1971).
7. J. J. Kirkland, *J. Chromatog. Sci.*, **9**, 206 (1971).
8. J. J. Kirkland, *J. Chromatog. Sci.*, **10**, 129 (1972).
9. J. H. Knox and J. F. Parcher, *Anal. Chem.*, **41**, 1599 (1969).
10. R. E. Majors, *J. Chromatog. Sci.*, **11**, 88 (1973).
11. J. J. Kirkland in "Gas Chromatography 1972," S. G. Perry, editor, Applied Science Publishers, Ltd., Essex, England, 1973.
12. J. J. Kirkland, *J. Chromatog.*, **83**, 149 (1973).
13. R. K. Iler and J. J. Kirkland, patents pending.
14. J. J. Kirkland and C. H. Dilks, Jr., *Anal. Chem.*, **45**, 1778 (1973).
15. J. J. Kirkland, *Anal. Chem.*, **43**, 36A (1971).
16. R. E. Majors, *Am. Laboratory*, pp. 27-39 (May, 1972).
17. R. E. Leitch and J. J. DeStefano, *J. Chromatog. Sci.*, **11**, 105 (1973).
18. J. J. Kirkland, *J. Agr. Food Chem.*, **21**, 171 (1973).
19. J. J. Kirkland, *J. Chromatog. Sci.*, **7**, 361 (1969).